Sex, Reproduction & Succession

Facebook page:

www.facebook.com/theforgottentudorwomen

Twitter:

https://twitter.com/SylviaBSo

Editorial services: Jennifer Quinlan

http://historicaleditorial.blogspot.com/

ISBN: 9798673062906

This book is dedicated to my daughter Amanda.

Contents

PROLOGUE: TWO ELIZABETHS

On 11 February 1503, Elizabeth of York, first Tudor Queen consort, died in the Tower of London at the age of thirty-seven following the premature birth of a daughter whom she named Katherine. One hundred years later, on 24 March 1603, Elizabeth's granddaughter and namesake, Elizabeth I, died at the age of sixty-nine, leaving England no heir to succeed her. Elizabeth I became known as the Virgin Queen because she never married and produced no children. The royal crown, won by Henry VII at the Battle of Bosworth in 1485, was inherited by Elizabeth's kinsman James VI of Scotland.

Elizabeth I inherited the crown upon her half sister's death in 1558 and was the last Tudor monarch to rule in England. Thus the Tudor dynasty that started with the fertile Queen Elizabeth of York ended with the barren Elizabeth I. There were many similarities between the two Elizabeths: both were born in purple as daughters of reigning kings, both were proclaimed illegitimate when the regime changed and both had the unquestionable right to succeed to the throne. Yet in the fifteenth century, it was unthinkable for a woman to ascend the English throne. That changed in the sixteenth century when the lack of male heirs meant that a woman not only could, but had to become Queen in her own right.

The Tudor dynasty died out because there was no heir of Elizabeth I's body to succeed her. Henry VIII, despite his six marriages, had produced no legitimate son who would live into old age. Three of the reigning Tudors (Edward VI, Mary I and Elizabeth I) died without heirs apparent, the most tragic case being that of Mary Tudor, who went through two recorded cases of phantom pregnancy. If it were not for physical frailty and the lack of reproductive health among the Tudors, the course of history might have been different.

This book concentrates on the medical downfall of the Tudors, examining their gynaecological history and medical records.

CHAPTER 1: EPIDEMIC DISEASES IN TUDOR ENGLAND

During the reign of the Tudors, England's population expanded rapidly. In 1524, there were some 2.3 million people living in the realm, and by 1601 there were more than four million.[1] In the minds of the sixteenth-century people, death was always present and lurking at every corner since life expectancy in Tudor England was just thirty-eight years. Even if one survived the dangers of the birth process and the first days of life, diseases such as diphtheria, whooping cough and measles presented mortal dangers. Life expectancy grew higher if a child survived until its fifth year, but older children and adults were at constant risk of death from accidents. A simple flesh wound could lead to death, considering the high risk of contracting tetanus or a deadly infection. Epidemic diseases swept through England on a regular basis, killing children and adults alike.

Although physicians in Tudor England had no knowledge of microorganisms and germs, it was widely understood that virulent diseases spread easily in dirty and cramped London, where people lived in close quarters. Henry VIII famously abhorred infectious diseases and left London for the countryside to escape epidemics. In July 1518, one worried observer wrote to Cardinal Thomas Wolsey that Henry VIII left London "for they do die in these parts in every place, not only of the smallpox and measles, but also of the great sickness [plague]".[2] Smallpox, measles and the plague were among the most dreaded infectious diseases of the Tudor period, and, as demonstrated in the abovementioned letter, they often spread at the same time.

Smallpox

The most infectious epidemic disease in Tudor England was smallpox. It originated in China or India some four thousand years ago. Smallpox was mentioned in sixth-century France, and by the sixteenth century it had been brought by travellers to England.[3] It's believed that the earliest references to smallpox in England occur in letters written in 1514 and 1518.[4] Henry VIII contracted smallpox in 1514 when he was twenty-two years old. In March 1514, Peter Martyr wrote that "Henry of England has had a fever; the physicians were afraid for his life, but it ended in the smallpox".[5] The King recovered quickly and without any serious complications.

People in Tudor England believed that the best way to protect oneself from an infectious disease was to avoid the company of infected individuals. In May 1528, for example, Henry VIII separated his mistress, Anne Boleyn, from other women at court because "my lady Princess and others of the Queen's maidens were sick of the smallpox".[6]

In 1544, physician Thomas Phaer wrote in his medical treatise *Regiment of Life*:

"[The signs of smallpox are] itch and fretting of the skin as if it had been rubbed with nettles, pain in the head and back, etc.: sometimes as it were a dry scab or lepry spreading over all the members, other whiles in pushes, pimples and whayls running with much corruption and matter, and with great pains of the face and throat, dryness of the tongue, hoarseness of the voice and, in some, quiverings of the heart with sownings."[7]

In October 1562, Queen Elizabeth I contracted smallpox and almost died of it. On 16 October 1562, it was reported that she had been very sick and not likely to survive:

"The Queen has been ill of fever at Kingston, and the malady has now turned to smallpox. The eruption cannot come out and she is in great danger. Cecil was hastily summoned from London at midnight. If the Queen die it will be very soon, within a few days at latest, and now all the talk is who is to be her successor."[8]

Elizabeth had a high fever and fell into a coma while the "palace people were all mourning for her as if she was already dead".[9] That night she rallied, and by 25 October she was convalescing and "only attending to the marks on her face to avoid disfigurement".[10] For those lucky ones who survived, immunity was lifelong, but many people were left disfigured with unsightly pockmarks. One observer reported that Queen Elizabeth was lucky to escape with not "many signs in her face".[11] She started using makeup to cover her "pits of smallpox", as she described them.[12] Mary Sidney, lady-in-waiting who nursed Elizabeth to health, also caught smallpox and recovered but was badly disfigured. Mary's husband later wrote:

"When I went to Newhaven I left her a full fair lady, in mine eye, at least, the fairest; and when I returned I found her as foul a lady as the smallpox could make her; which she did take by continual attendance of her Majesty's most precious person (sick of the same disease), the scars of which (to her resolute discomfort) ever since hath done and doth remain in her face, so as she lives solitarily *sicut nicticorax in domicilio suo* [like a night-raven in the house], more to my charge than if we had boarded together, as we did before that evil accident happened."[13]

Today it is known that smallpox was caused by one of two virus variants, *Variola major* and *Variola minor*. The risk of death upon contracting the disease was about thirty percent, with higher rates among babies. The smallpox vaccine, introduced by Edward Jenner in 1796, was the first successful vaccine to be developed. Jenner observed that milkmaids who previously had caught cowpox, a closely related animal disease, did not catch smallpox. Jenner used pus from cowpox to inoculate eight-year-old James Phipps, which resulted in immunity to smallpox.

The Plague

Another infectious disease rife in Tudor England was the plague that was often known in the sixteenth century as "the great sickness". Now known to have been caused by the bacteria *Yersinia pestis* and spread by fleas carried on rats' backs, the plague known then as "the Black Death" first appeared in the fourteenth century and peaked in Europe from 1347 to 1351. It was one of the most devastating pandemics in human history, taking between 75 to 200 million lives throughout the world. The plague was endemic in Europe since 1351 and appeared regularly in England during the Tudor period. The plague manifests itself by painful, swollen lymph nodes, usually in the armpits or groin. Other symptoms include fever, headache, chills, muscle aches and fatigue. The plague is still common throughout the world: between 2010 and 2015, the World Health Organisation reported that 3,248 people were infected with this disease, with 584 dying.[14] It can now be treated with antibiotics, and therefore scientists estimate that the plague does not have the potential to cause a global pandemic.

Letters, documents, papers and wills are brimming with references to the plague. In January 1518, Henry VIII, who obsessively feared contagion, issued royal plague regulations. These regulations set out ways in which plague was to be controlled, such as the marking of affected houses, sick individuals denied access to unaffected localities and basic sanitation measures to be carried out. Henry VIII feared infection, and whenever there was an outbreak he moved with his most trusted servants several times in an attempt to isolate his entire household from the source of infection. In 1517, for instance, the Venetian red, flat and itchy rash that usually starts on the face and then spreads to the rest of the body is a typical sign of measles. Complications of measles are relatively common, ranging from mild ones such as diarrhoea to serious ones such as pneumonia, croup, otitis media, acute brain inflammation and corneal ulceration. The disease is especially dangerous to pregnant women and small children. The disease has been known since at least the ninth century and today can be prevented through vaccination. The first measles vaccine was introduced in 1963.

Measles was endemic in Tudor England. In 1489, it was reported that "that season there were the measles so strong, and in especial amongst the ladies and the gentlewomen, that some died of that sickness".[25] It appears that people in the sixteenth century didn't know that the survivors of measles obtained lifelong immunity, as is clear from the letter of Sir Piers Eggecombe to Thomas Cromwell: "Frances Palmer, one of my wife's women, lying on a pallet in her own chamber, is sick of the measles, so I will not presume to come into the King's presence nor to the Commons house."[26]

Henry VIII had measles in 1514 but still avoided people who were infected with this disease and was adamant about protecting his loved ones. In April 1535, he left London and sent Anne Boleyn to Hampton Court Palace when one of her ladies-in-waiting caught measles.[27] Some royal children died of measles: in France, Charles VIII's heir, Dauphin Charles Orlando, passed away in 1495 at three years old, and Francis I's eight-year-old daughter Charlotte died in 1524 after experiencing a high fever that accompanied measles.

The most famous Tudor who suffered from measles was Edward VI. On 2 April 1552, Edward recorded in his diary that he "fell sick of the measles and the smallpox".[28] On 12 April, he wrote to his friend Barnaby Fitzpatrick that: "We have a little been troubled with smallpox, which hath letted [precluded] us to write hitherto; but now we have shaken that quite away."[29] The King died in July 1553 after battling a long and exhausting disease that made him cough violently and disfigured his body so much so that he was bald and covered with ulcers at the time of his death. It's likely that Edward VI died of tuberculosis and that, as suggested by modern research, measles that he suffered from in 1552 had suppressed his natural immunity to tuberculosis.

grievous hurt to the King's people . . . who cannot discern the cunning [learned] from the uncunning."[4]

In 1540, the King granted a royal charter to the United Company of Barber-Surgeons, merging the two companies, the Mystery of Barbers and Company of Pure Surgeons. Barber-surgeons previously performed surgical procedures including bloodletting, cupping therapy, pulling teeth and amputation, but in 1540 they were prohibited from applying "outward remedies".[5] Barbers, at the bottom of the structure, performed shaving and teeth pulling.

Plate 1: "Henry VIII and the Barber Surgeons": This painting shows the King celebrating the Act of Union between the Company of Barbers and the Guild or Fellowship of Surgeons in 1540.

"A patient cannot be cured who will not trust his physician, but takes ignorantly what medicines he likes himself", Henry VIII once said.[6] The King surrounded himself with a group of trusted, university-trained physicians whom he generously rewarded for their work. Upon his accession in 1509, Henry appointed Thomas Linacre as his physician, awarding him with £50 per annum. Linacre served as Prince Arthur's tutor and physician and taught Princess Mary Italian. He translated Galen's works into English, earning praise from Desiderius Erasmus. After Linacre died in 1524, John Chambre and William Butts were the King's favourite physicians and close friends. During the outbreak of the sweating sickness in 1528, Henry wrote to Anne Boleyn that Dr Chambre was "the physician in whom I trust most". When Anne caught the dreaded sweat, Chambre was absent, so Henry sent Anne his second-best, Dr Butts, advising her to "be guided by his advice in your illness".[7] Both Chambre and Butts were trusted with the birth of the King's only legitimate male heir, Prince Edward, and attended Jane Seymour, Henry's favourite wife, in her last hours.[8] Born c. 1485, Dr Butts was some six years the King's senior and served as his court physician until his death in 1545. Butts's death prompted the imperial ambassador's worry over Henry VIII's health: "I do not know what will come of it, as his principal medical man, Dr Butts, died this winter."[9]

Plate 2: William Butts, one of Henry VIII's favourite physicians.

Henry VIII was interested in medicine and created his own medicines. It's been sometimes suggested that he developed an interest in medicine as a result of his own poor health. Yet Henry VIII's serious health issues started after his 1536 injury at the tiltyard, whereas his interest in medicine dates from before that. The King's letters indicate that he offered medical advice to his courtiers, especially the high-ranking officials and favourites. In June 1528, Sir Brian Tuke wrote to Cardinal Wolsey:

> "And coming to that, Your Grace wrote, to be sorry of my disease, whereof I most humbly thank Your Grace, His Highness began to tell me a medicine *pro tumour* [for swelling], saving Your Grace's honour, *testiculorum* [of testicles]. I immediately said, His Highness was not well-informed of my disease, which is not there, but in vesica [bladder], and proceeded *ex calore in renibus* [from the heat of kidneys]. His Highness . . . showed me the remedies as any most cunning physician in England could do."[10]

Henry also advised Tuke to instruct Cardinal Wolsey how to behave during the epidemic. The cardinal was to avoid infectious air, and if anyone in his household fell sick, Wolsey should "remove to a clean [unaffected by infection] place . . . with a small and clean [healthy] company". Henry also advised to eat light suppers, drink wine moderately and "use the pills of Rasis", probably Rhases, an Arabian physician, once a week.[11] Henry devised a "medicine for the pestilence" and several others to ease the pain in his legs.

answers thereunto and likewise that a woman might meddle [cohabit] with a man and yet conceive no child unless she would for herself."[15]

When it comes to contraception and abortion, historians are left in the dark because there is very little written evidence concerning both. The Catholic Church condemned such practices, though some individuals chose to believe that since the infant did not receive its soul until after forty days of gestation, an early abortion was less "sinful" than a later one. Some scholars assert that the English in the sixteenth century resorted to "practising coitus interruptus . . . and no doubt procuring many abortions, possibly also infanticide".[16] There is no way of knowing for sure since people were not writing about such matters, and if they were practised, then information and advice were certainly transmitted by word of mouth.

Although the cessation of menstruation was one of many signs of pregnancy, in an age of no pregnancy tests women were sure about their condition only after they felt their child's movement, called "quickening". Quickening was the moment when it was believed that the infant acquired a soul, and an abortion after this time was not allowed. Quickening was also believed to be a sign that the baby was alive and well. When Jane Seymour's baby quickened in May 1537, five months before the birth, Henry VIII ordered the *Te Deum* to be sung "for joy of the Queen's quickening".[17]

Sometimes quickening caused pain, like in the case of Anne Boleyn's first pregnancy. Lancelot de Carle, the French diplomat who wrote a poem about Anne Boleyn's life and death shortly after her execution in 1536, claimed that: "When she began to feel the baby's little feet moving inside her, oh, she learned very well to complain and to whine, in a pitiful voice with trembling words, to show the pain she had!"[18] He went on to say that Anne suffered so much that Henry VIII was so worried that de Carle believed he "wanted his daughter dead" to save Anne's life.[19] It is impossible to assess the truthfulness of this story because de Carle is the only source that mentions difficulties with Anne Boleyn's first pregnancy.

Interesting details of quickening are contained in Katherine Parr's letter to her husband, Thomas Seymour:

"I gave your little knave your blessing, who like an honest man stirred apace after and before, for Mary Odell, being abed with me, had laid her hand upon my belly to feel it stir. It hath stirred these three days every morning and evening, so that I trust when ye come it will make you some pastime."[20]

The quickening was usually impatiently awaited by expectant mothers, as shown in the letter of John Paston III in 1472. He wrote that my "Lady of Norfolk is with child . . . she waits the quickening within these six weeks at the farthest".[21] Quickening usually occurred around the fourth month of pregnancy, and if the baby did not move at this time, it was believed that it was either dead or not ready to quicken yet. When Anne Boleyn was arrested in May 1536, she "much lamented my Lady of Worcester" because "her child did not stir in her body". When asked by one of her ladies-in-waiting "what should be the cause of it", Anne replied that it was caused by "the sorrow she took for me", although Lady Worcester gave birth to a healthy baby girl several months later.[22]

Infertility

In an age when pregnancy and motherhood defined women's status, infertility was a personal tragedy for many sixteenth-century couples, especially royal ones. The most famous Renaissance woman who struggled to conceive was Catherine de Medici, who married Francis I's son, the future Henri II. The death of the French King's eldest son in 1536 brought Catherine's infertility into sharper relief. She surrounded herself with the most skilled doctors but also listened to the advice of astrologers and magicians. The prescribed medicines she drank every day ranged from mild herbal potions to smelly concoctions made from the urine of pregnant animals and the powdered sexual organs of boars, stags and cats. She also drank potions made of a mixture of animal milk and blood, with additions of unicorn's horn and vinegar.[23] The Venetian ambassador Dandolo remarked that although Catherine swallowed "all possible medicines that might aid conception", she was, in his opinion, "more at risk of increasing her difficulty than finding the solution".[24] She finally gave birth for the first time in 1544.

Infertility wasn't taboo. In 1536, Sir John Wallop, who served as ambassador to the French court, congratulated his friend Viscount Lisle on his wife's pregnancy. "I rejoice first for both your sakes", he wrote, adding, "and secondly, because it gives hope both to my wife and me, considering not to be so long married as you two, and either of us being younger, man for man and woman for woman; trusting, if we return once quietly to the castle, such good fortune may ensue unto us".[25]

Infertile couples resorted to medicine, but religion played its part as well. The intercession of saints as well as pilgrimages to holy shrines were believed beneficial in aiding conception.

Prenatal care & diet

Contemporaneous documents indicate that pregnant women were advised to adhere to a diet and keep physically active. From a letter written to Lady Honour Lisle by her French physician, Dr Le Coop, in 1538, we learn that the diet was tailored according to an individual's unique humoral makeup. The idea of the four humours was at the base of Tudor medicine. It dated back to ancient Greek doctors, particularly Galen and Hippocrates. They believed that four elements made up all things: earth, air, fire and water. Each of these elements had a corresponding quality: earth was cold and dry, air was hot and moist, fire hot and dry and water cold and moist. An imbalance of these elements caused disease. Identifying one's humoral makeup helped during the process of healing and was also useful during pregnancy.

The English edition of *The Birth of Mankind* reveals what kind of food and drink was believed to have had beneficial effects on pregnant women. There were two types of diets. The first one was observed "the month before her labour or longer" while the second was to be observed "in the time of labour".[26] In general, a pregnant woman was advised "to take good heed to her diet, that she take things the which may comfort and strengthen the body, feeding not overmuch of anything, and to drink pleasant and well-savouring wine or other drink".[27]

Dietary preferment depended on how an individual woman felt during pregnancy. If, for example, she had problems with constipation, her diet should consist of "apples fried with sugar taken fasting [on an empty stomach] in the morning, and after that a draught of pure wine alone, or else tempered with the juice of sweet and very ripe apples". Eating figs was believed to "loose the belly without peril".[28] Women were also advised what to avoid during pregnancy if they had problems with constipation; eating "meats broiled or roasted, and rice, hard eggs, beef, chestnuts, and all sour fruits" was strongly dissuaded.

The second type of diet was believed to "cause the birth or labour to be very easy" and alleviate pain.[29]

Physical exercise was also recommended as part of the regimen. A pregnant woman was encouraged "moderately to exercise the body in doing something, stirring, moving, going [walking] or standing, more than otherwise she was wont to do". During the early stages of labour, she was also encouraged to "to sit still; then (rising again), to go up and down a flight of stairs, crying or reaching [clearing her throat] so loud as she can, so to stir herself"; this should take about an hour.[30] In his letter written to the heavily pregnant Katherine Parr in the summer of 1548, Thomas Seymour reminded her of the importance of physical exercise and diet:

"I do desire your Highness to keep the little knave so lean and gaunt with your good diet and walking, that he may be so small that he may creep out of a mouse hole."[31]

It looks like Thomas Seymour believed that by controlling her weight, and hence the infant's weight, through exercise and diet, Katherine Parr could assure the newborn an easy passage through the birthing canal. Katherine Parr was already thirty-six at the time of her first pregnancy, and it is clear from the letters she received from her correspondents that she suffered at that period. Katherine's two stepdaughters, Ladies Mary and Elizabeth, were worried about her. In the weeks before the birth of Katherine's child, Mary Tudor wrote: "I trust to hear good news of your Grace's great belly; and in the meantime shall desire much to hear of your health, which I pray almighty God to continue and increase to his pleasure as much as your own heart can desire." Lady Elizabeth's letter reveals concern; Katherine was "so great with child, and so sickly" that she could hardly sit down to write a letter.[32] It's possible that Katherine suffered from *hyperemesis gravidarum*, a form of acute morning sickness. She gave birth to her daughter, Mary Seymour, on 30 August 1548, but died several days later.

Miscarriage

The sixteenth-century ideal of hereditary monarchy required that kings had to produce healthy male successors, but in an age of poor medical care, miscarriages were frequent occurrences. The Tudors attributed miscarriages to several factors. In an English translation of *The Birth of Mankind,* the following passage is devoted to this topic:

"Item, aborsement [miscarriage] may happen by overmuch stirring of the body in labouring [working], dancing, or leaping; or by some fall or thrust against some wall, or beating; or by some sudden anger, fear, dread, sorrow, or some sudden and unlooked for joy."[33]

Pregnant women were therefore advised to avoid a surfeit of activity, rest often and avoid sudden fright, anger or sorrow. In July 1533, when Henry VIII received unfavourable news from Rome, he kept the news secret from the heavily pregnant Anne Boleyn so that she would be "spared any sorrow and disappointment likely to endanger the life of the child she bears in her womb".[34]

Many queens used this rationalisation to explain their miscarriages. When Anne Boleyn miscarried a son in January 1536, she attributed this tragedy to two factors. First was the brusque way her uncle, the Duke of Norfolk, informed her about Henry VIII's dangerous accident in the tiltyard several days before the miscarriage.[35] The second was the fact that Anne loved Henry so much that whenever she saw him dallying with other women she was heartbroken.[36] Anne was referring to Henry VIII's extramarital affair with her maid of honour, Jane Seymour. Some sources say that she caught Jane sitting on the King's lap and exclaimed: "I saw this harlot Jane sitting on your knees while my belly was doing its duty!"[37] Men also sought to rationalise miscarriages. Henry VIII always attributed his wives' misfortunes in the birthing chamber to the will of God. Soon after Anne's miscarriage, the King told one of his confidantes: "I see that God will not give me male children."

When he visited Anne's bedchamber, he was cold towards her and informed her that he would speak with her when she recovered her health.[38]

If a woman miscarried but her body didn't expel the foetus, she was given pennyroyal that caused uterine contractions (pennyroyal was also known as an abortifacient). Tansy was given to women to prevent miscarriage.

Childbirth

Plate 3: A woman giving birth on a birthing stool from Eucharius Rösslin's *Birth of Mankind*.

Childbirth in the sixteenth century was regulated by a series of elaborately codified protocols. In 1494, Henry VII drew up a series of ordinances governing the smooth running of the royal household. Authorship of these ordinances is usually ascribed to Henry VII's mother, Lady Margaret Beaufort, Countess of Richmond and Derby, although she most likely didn't draw them up.[39] The ordinances included regulations concerning preparations for "deliverances of the Queen". According to the ritual prescribed within, the Queen should first choose the location of her "laying-in", the location wherein she would establish her birthing chamber. The birthing chamber didn't refer to one room but to a suite on the Queen's side of the royal palaces. The birthing space was carefully and lavishly decorated with luxurious items such as tapestries, furniture and chattels. When Anne Boleyn was preparing her birthing chamber at Greewnich Palace in 1533, Henry VIII loaned her "one of the richest and most triumphant beds which was given for the ransom of the Duke of Alençon".[40] Borrowing items to furnish birthing chambers wasn't unusual: Lady Honor Lisle, for instance, planned to borrow a variety of luxurious objects from the royal wardrobe for her confinement.[41]

Tapestries were advised to cover up all of the walls and windows within the chamber where the Queen would give birth. One window was permitted to be left uncovered so that "she may have light when it pleased her".[42] In 1533, carpenters made "a false roof in the Queen's Bedchamber for to seal it and hang it with cloth of arras", and a heavy "cupboard of state" was brought in to display gold plate, gilded crucifixes and images for the altar.[43]

The bed, linen and hangings were especially important. Birthing stools—chairs with a hole in them—were used in England, although there's no direct evidence that Tudor queens or noblewomen laboured using such stools. The Queen's "great bed" had the finest bedding and embroideries.[44] The "pallet bed" mentioned in the ordinances could have been the bed where the Queen would give birth and then she would move to the main bed to recover. It's more likely, however, that the Queen's trusted lady-in-waiting known as her "bedfellow" would sleep on the pallet bed in the Queen's bedchamber to serve her royal mistress whenever needed during the night.

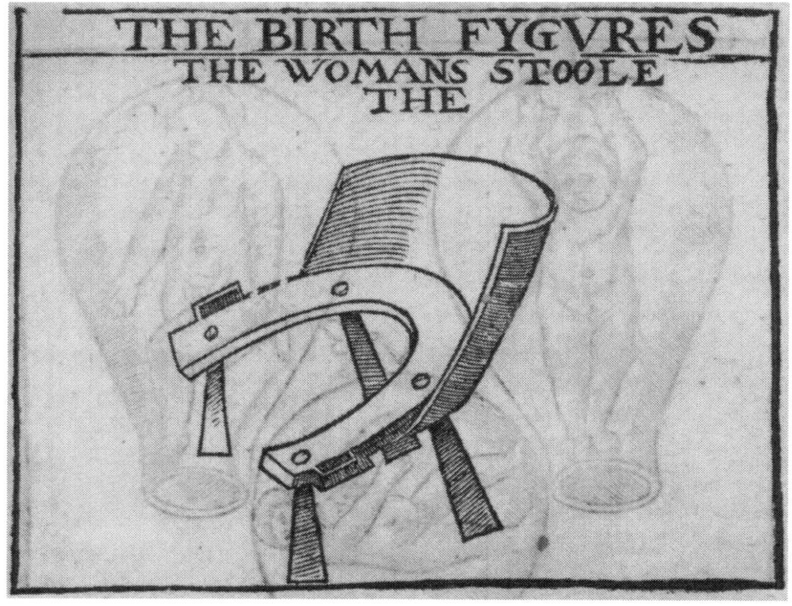

Plate 4: Birthing stool from Eucharius Rösslin's *Birth of Mankind.*

About a month before their due date, Tudor queens retired from public life by "taking to their chamber". The ceremony started with a public Mass in the royal chapel. After the Mass, a procession of lords and ladies escorted the Queen to the door of her private apartments, where the company would take refreshment of "spice and wine under the cloth of estate". Then two of the highest-ranking peers of the realm ceremoniously led the Queen to the chamber wherein she would give birth and took leave of her. Then all of the Queen's ladies-in-waiting joined her inside, "and after that no man [was] to come into the chamber where she shall be delivered, save women; and they be made all manner of officers, as butlers, pantlers, sewers, carvers, cupbearers, and all manner of officers shall bring to them all manner of things to the Great Chamber door, and the women officers for to receive it in the chamber".[45]

In 1555, when Queen Mary I took to her chamber, the Spanish ambassador Simon Renard observed: "This is an ancient custom in England whenever a princess is about to be confined: to remain in retirement forty days before and forty days after."[46] Mary was the last Tudor queen who "took to her chamber" but no child was born as she suffered from a phantom pregnancy.[47]

Childbirth was a predominantly female affair, and no men, not even doctors (unless there were complications), were allowed within this female sanctum. This is well-illustrated by the circumstances of Elizabeth of York's birth in February 1466. Dr Dominic de Serigo, who assured the King that Elizabeth Woodville was expecting a son, wanted to be the first person to pass the news of the birth of the prince to the King, but since he wasn't allowed inside the birthing chamber, he waited outside. When he heard the baby's first cries, he "knocked or called secretly at the chamber door, and frayned [asked] what the Queen had".

One of the ladies who attended the Queen's delivery told him that "whatsoever the Queen's grace hath here within, sure it is that a fool stands there without", and so Dr de Serigo left without passing the news of the birth of a daughter to Edward IV.[48]

That male physicians waited beyond the door of the birthing chamber is further confirmed by an illustration of Henry VI's birth in the fifteenth-century Middle English biography of Richard Beauchamp entitled *The Pageants of Richard Beauchamp, Earl of Warwick,* showing various scenes from his life and the lives of kings and queens he served.[49] The illustration depicting Henry VI's birth shows the tightly swaddled infant held in the arms of a lady-in-waiting. In the lower right side of the folio, we see one of the Queen's female servants, perhaps a midwife, standing in the doorway and informing a man, either a physician or a messenger, about the birth of a prince.[50]

Midwives took oaths and received practising licences from the Bishop of London or the Dean of St Paul's. Ecclesiastical licensing of midwives started soon after Henry VIII's 1512 Medical Act and continued until 1642.[51] In his 1547 *Breviary of Health*, Andrew Boorde wrote that "every midwife should be presented with honest women of great gravity to the Bishop". These women would attest with their own names that the candidate was "a sad [respectable] woman, wise and discreet, having experience, and worthy to have the office of a midwife". Based on the presented evidence, the bishop would then deliberate with "a doctor of physick" who would examine the candidate's knowledge and "instruct her in that thing that she is ignorant".[52] If a woman was judged competent, she would then be questioned about her knowledge of midwifery by the Archbishop of Canterbury, as the oath taken by one Eleanor Peade in 1567 shows. Eleanor was also separately examined by eight women, presumably experienced midwives.[53]

The Church gave midwives the authority to baptise or sprinkle infants with holy water if they judged that the baby was weak and could die following birth. When the Duke of Norfolk's daughter-in-law prematurely gave birth to a boy in March 1538, the duke intended to ask the King to be a godfather, "but now the women here would not suffer me to let the child be so long unchristened."[54] Midwives stayed with the new mothers often until after the baptism. Jane Seymour's midwife and wet nurse attended Prince Edward's baptism on 15 October 1537.[55]

Queens selected midwives from among the women who attended the births of bourgeois women of London society. In 1534, one Mistress Burgyn told Joan Hammulden, the midwife who attended her delivery, that "for her honesty and her cunning she might be midwife unto the Queen of England, if it were Queen Katharine; and if it were Queen Anne, she was too good to be her midwife, for she was a whore and a harlot of her living".[56] Royals often paid rewards to the midwives of their female friends. In 1532, Henry VIII paid the unnamed "nurse and the midwife of Sir Nicholas Harvey's child" out of his Privy Purse expenses.[57] This was likely on Anne Boleyn's behest, as Sir Harvey's wife, Bridget Wiltshire, was her close friend. Similar payment was made "to the nurse and to the midwife of my Lady of Worcester, by way of reward" in February 1530.[58] Again, the Countess of Worcester was Anne Boleyn's close confidante. Mary Tudor's Privy Purse expenses also contain countless examples of monetary rewards and gifts for the wet nurses and midwives of her friends.[59]

Several names of midwives attending royalty were recorded. In 1469, Margaret Cobb, midwife to Edward IV's Queen, Elizabeth Woodville, received in addition to her fee a life pension of £10 a year, as did Alice Massey, who attended Elizabeth of York in her last delivery in 1503.[60] Male physicians didn't directly intervene during childbirth, but their presence was required within the palace where the Queen gave birth so they could help if any complications arose. When Elizabeth of York went into premature labour in the Tower of London on 2 February 1503, her midwife, Alice Massey, was present and the baby princess was hastily baptised immediately after the birth in the church of St Peter ad Vincula. When the Queen's health deteriorated, Dr Hallysworth was ordered to come from Kent "by the King's commandment" but couldn't save Elizabeth of York, who died shortly afterwards.[61] Likewise, when Jane Seymour's labour lasted far too long, three trusted male physicians were admitted to her birthing chamber and attended Jane on her deathbed.[62]

Although in the sixteenth-century mind-set labour pains were ordained by God because of Eve's transgression in the Garden of Eden, women took a keen interest in remedies that soothed pain and made the contractions more bearable. Then, as now, women feared long and painful labour, infertility and miscarriage. Midwives usually were skilled in using herbs to help in all sorts of gynaecological ailments: betony was used to reduce labour pains, columbine to speed delivery, horehound to ease labour. Catherine de Medici, Queen Regent of France, ordered a special brew to be administered to her daughter Elisabeth during the strongest contractions. Elisabeth's husband, Philip of Spain, fed her with the brew and "this had such a force that the said Lady was delivered straightaway afterwards, without feeling the slightest pain".[63] In England, women in labour restored their strength with a drink called caudle, a spiced and sweetened wine.[64]

Women also resorted to spiritual help. In an age when religion and magic mixed freely, relics and gemstones were believed to be helpful during labour. In December 1502, Elizabeth of York paid a monk of Westminster Abbey for bringing her the girdle of Our Lady the Virgin.[65] According to the legend, the Virgin Mary threw down her girdle, a decorative belt worn around the waist, to St Thomas before she went into heaven. According to fifteenth-century chronicler John Flete, Edward the Confessor presented the girdle to Westminster Abbey. The monks kept this precious relic in a crystal coffer.[66]

Female girdles were often made of stones with apotropaic qualities. Coral, jet and amber were thought to have properties helpful for labouring women.[67] Isabella of Portugal, wife of the Holy Roman Emperor Charles V and niece of Katharine of Aragon, clutched St Elizabeth's girdle when in labour and acquired a collection of relics associated with easing pain during childbirth, having them in her birthing chamber as she delivered her children.[68]

Many Tudor women died as a direct result of childbirth. Some died during or shortly after labour, others suffered for days or weeks before finally succumbing to death. Puerperal fever "affected women within the first three days after childbirth and progressed rapidly, causing acute symptoms of severe abdominal pain, fever and debility". The term "puerperal fever" was coined in the early eighteenth century.[69]

When a woman died as a result of childbearing, her contemporaries usually stated that she died "in childbed".[70] There were various causes for maternal death during or shortly after delivery. The most common cause was postpartum infection, referred to as childbed fever. It was a bacterial infection of the female reproductive tract following childbirth. The most common infection was that of the uterus and surrounding tissues, known as puerperal sepsis. Risk factors included the presence of certain bacteria such as group B streptococcus in the vagina, premature rupture of membranes, manual removal of the placenta and prolonged labour, among others. Haemorrhage during or after labour was also a common occurrence.

Additionally, the lack of proper hand hygiene contributed to the risk of maternal death. It wasn't until the nineteenth century when Ignaz Semmelweis, a Hungarian obstetrician working at the Vienna General Hospital, observed that it was not the actual labour that killed women but doctors' dirty hands spreading infections. Physicians didn't wash their hands after touching dead bodies, contaminating women's privy parts with harmful bacteria.

Caesarean section

If a woman died during labour, or if it was clear she would not survive her ordeal, midwives were allowed to perform a Caesarean section to save the life of the baby.[71] More commonly, however, a midwife would call a surgeon to perform the operation. In the late sixteenth century, it was rumoured that Jane Seymour underwent a Caesarean section, but it's highly unlikely that she was cut open and lived for twelve days before dying.[72] It's widely accepted that no successful Caesarean section on a living woman was recorded in England until 1793.[73]

A little known manuscript preserved in the British Library shows that Elizabeth Holland, maid of honour to Anne Boleyn and Jane Seymour, underwent a Caesarean section in 1548. Elizabeth Holland, known commonly as Bess, was a mistress of Thomas Howard, third Duke of Norfolk, from 1527 until Norfolk's disgrace and arrest in 1546. In 1547, she married Henry Reppes and soon became pregnant. Simon Lowe, merchant tailor in the City of London, wrote to his friend Mr Andros that Elizabeth "died with child and the child was ripped out of her belly and the said Harry Reppes said that the child was alive and died immediately". The truth of the matter—whether Bess and her child were alive or dead at the time of the Caesarean section—was a bone of contention. If Henry Reppes could prove that the child was alive, he would have been entitled to the use of her lands for life. Lowe wrote: "I will not blame Harry Reppes though he will make the surgeon and the midwife say that there was life in the child for he shall have all her land by the law of the realm during his life." Lowe also thought that it was highly unlikely that Bess was alive during the operation: "The truth is the woman was dead half an hour afore the surgeon did rip her." He also affirmed that the physicians and midwife who attended her in childbirth were of the same opinion.

Lowe's motives to claim that both Bess and her child were dead at the time of the "ripping of her", as he referred to the Caesarean section, were dictated by financial gain. With no heir, Bess's brother Thomas was entitled to claim her lands, and Lowe bought them from Thomas at a great sum. Lowe asked Andros if he could make some inquiries in Mendham and Harleston about what went on in Bess's birthing chamber, adding the names of the surgeons and midwife who witnessed her death. Phillipa Con of Mendham was the midwife, Richard Spayne of Harleston was "the surgeon that ripped her" and Edmund Hall (of Harleston or Mendham) was "the surgeon that would not rip her".[74] This small listing shows that surgeons were not always keen to perform a Caesarean operation, especially if a woman was still alive. There were also other people present "at the ripping of her", but Lowe didn't remember their names. At the end of his letter, Lowe added that a man by the name William Rochester tried to bribe the surgeons and midwife to say that "the child was alive". Rochester was "the falsest and the craftiest man that is in this country and if you handle him well and promise him a few shillings, he will tell you the truth".[75] This, Lowe said, could be achieved in a tavern where Rochester would drink and talk in the presence of witnesses.

Wet-nursing

Tudor queens and noblewomen customarily didn't breastfeed their infants. The choice of a wet nurse was a weighty matter since it was believed that her characteristics might flow into the infant during breastfeeding. A wet nurse was chosen from among women who were still lactating and had to be of gentle birth, good-natured, attractive and, above all, healthy. Elizabeth of York interviewed two women for the post of wet nurse in 1502, Mistress Harcourt at Westminster and a "French woman" at Baynard's Castle.[76]

Women often recommended their friends for the post, as illustrated by a report in 1601 by an anonymous author who wrote: "My mother was chosen and brought to the Court by my Lady Herbert of Troy, to have been her Majesty's [Elizabeth I's] nurse, and had been chosen before all other had her gracious mother had her own will therein."[77] Whereas Anne Boleyn did not choose a wet nurse, she worked in unison with Blanche, Lady Herbert of Troy, who served as one of Elizabeth's governesses and recommended the rejected candidate.

Wet nurses were usually held in great esteem. In December 1502, nineteen years after her brother's birth,

Elizabeth of York paid for three and a half yards of cloth to "a woman that was nurse to the Prince, brother to the Queen's Grace".[78] Katherine Gibbes, Prince Arthur's wet nurse, received £20 of a grant-for-life in April 1490, paid from Henry VII's Exchequer.[79]

Churching

Churching represented thanksgiving, cleansing and re-entry into society following childbirth. Churching usually occurred thirty to forty days after birth, in emulation of the Virgin Mary, who presented Jesus in the Temple in Jerusalem forty days after his birth to fulfil the requirements of the Law of Moses. While pre-Tudor churching ceremonies are well-recorded—there are descriptions of Margaret of Anjou's in 1453 and Elizabeth Woodville's in 1466—no churching descriptions survive for the Tudor queens. What is known is that churching required a new set of clothes for the Queen and her ladies-in-waiting.[80]

NOTES

[1] Eucharius Rösslin, Thomas Raynalde, *The Birth of Mankind*, p. 57.
[2] *Calendar of State Papers, Venice,* Volume 6, n. 884.
[3] Ibid., Volume 4, n. 664.
[4] James Hillman, *The Myth of Analysis: Three Essays in Archetypal Psychology*, p. 253.

[5] Read more about Katharine's obstetrical history in Chapter 7.
[6] *Calendar of State Papers, Venice,* Volume 6, n. 884.
[7] *Calendar of State Papers, Spain,* Volume 3, n. 189.
[8] Tracy Borman, *Elizabeth's Women*, p. 209.
[9] Jane Malcolm-Davies and Ninya Mikhaila, *The Tudor Tailor*, p. 24.
[10] Joan Larsen Klein, *Daughters, Wives, and Widows*, p. 178.
[11] Eucharius Rösslin, Thomas Raynalde, *The Birth of Mankind,* p. 23.
[12] *Calendar of State Papers, Spain,* Volume 2, n. 163.
[13] Nicola Tallis, *Uncrowned Queen: The Fateful Life of Margaret Beaufort, Tudor Matriarch*, p. 4.
[14] *Calendar of State Papers, Spain,* Volume 1, n. 210.
[15] Retha M. Warnicke, *Wicked Women of Tudor England*, p. 55.
[16] E. A. Wrigley, *Family Limitation in Pre-Industrial England*, p. 104.
[17] Read more about Jane Seymour's obstetrical history in Chapter 13.
[18] Susan Walters Schmid, *Anne Boleyn, Lancelot de Carle, and the Uses of Documentary Evidence*, p. 117.
[19] Ibid.
[20] Jane Mueller, *Katherine Parr: Complete Works and Correspondence*, p. 170.
[21] Norman Davis, *The Paston Letters: A Selection in Modern Spelling*, p. 210.
[22] *Letters and Papers*, Henry VIII, Volume 10, n. 793.
[23] Jennifer Grodetsky, Ronald Rabinowitz, Jeanne O'Brien. *The "Infertility" of Catherine de Medici and Its Influence on 16th Century France*, p. 8.
[24] Princess Michael of Kent, *The Serpent and the Moon*, p. 196.
[25] *Letters and Papers, Foreign and Domestic, Henry VIII,* Volume 11, n. 1342.
[26] Eucharius Rösslin, Thomas Raynalde, *The Birth of Mankind*, p. 106.
[27] Ibid.
[28] Ibid., p. 104.
[29] Ibid.
[30] Ibid., pp. 105-06.
[31] Janel Mueller, *Katherine Parr: Complete Works and Correspondence,* p. 168.
[32] Susan James, *Catherine Parr*, p. 292.
[33] Rösslin, Raynalde, *The Birth of Mankind*, p. 138.
[34] *Calendar of State Papers, Spain,* Volume 4 Part 2, n. 1107.
[35] *Calendar of State Papers, Spain,* Volume 5 Part 2, n. 21.
[36] Ibid., n. 29.
[37] Eric Ives, *The Life and Death of Anne Boleyn*, p. 304.

38 *Calendar of State Papers, Spain,* Volume 5 Part 2, n. 29.
39 For doubts about the authorship, see Kay Staniland, "Royal Entry into the World", in *England in the Fifteenth Century: Proceedings of the 1992 Harlaxton Symposium*, ed. Daniel Williams (Woodbridge, UK: Boydell, 1987), pp. 297-313, at p. 299.
40 *Letters and Papers, Henry VIII,* Volume 6, n. 1069.
41 Catherine Mann, "Clothing Bodies, Dressing Rooms: Fashioning Fecundity in The Lisle Letters" in *Parergon (Journal of the Australian and New Zealand Associating of Medieval and Early Modern Studies)*, January 2005, pp. 137-157.
42 *A Collection of Ordinances*, p. 125.
43 David Starkey, *Six Wives*, p. 505.
44 *A Collection of Ordinances*, p. 125.
45 Ibid.
46 *Calendar of State Papers, Spain,* Volume 13, n. 178.
47 Read more about Mary's two phantom pregnancies in Chapter 20.
48 Robert Fabyan, *The New Chronicles of England and France*, p. 655.
49 BL, Cotton MS Julius E IV/3.
50 BL, Cotton MS Julius E IV/3, f. 22v.
51 Thomas R. Forbes, "The Regulation of English Midwives in the Sixteenth and Seventeenth Centuries", p. 23 in Philip K. Wilson (ed.) *Childbirth: The Medicalization of Obstetrics* (Taylor & Francis, 1996).
52 Ibid.
53 Ibid.
54 *Letters and Papers, Foreign and Domestic, Henry VIII,* Volume 13 Part 1, n. 504.
55 *Letters and Papers, Foreign and Domestic, Henry VIII,* Volume 12 Part 2, n. 911.
56 *Letters and Papers, Foreign and Domestic, Henry VIII,* Volume 7, n. 2.
57 Sir Nicholas Harris Nicolas, *Privy Purse Expenses of Henry VIII*, p. 197.
58 Ibid., p. 22.
59 Frederic Madden, *Privy Purse Expenses of the Princess Mary*, pp. 11, 16, 19, 45, 55, 61, 66, 71.
60 *Parliament Rolls of Medieval England, Edward IV: October 1472,* n. 14.
61 Sir Nicholas Harris Nicolas, *Privy Purse Expenses of Elizabeth of York*, pp. 62, 96.
62 *State Papers*, Volume 1, p. 572.
63 "Women's Little Secrets": Defining the Boundaries of Reproductive Knowledge in Sixteenth-Century France: Society for the Social History of Medicine Student Essay Competition Winner, 1999, *Social History of Medicine*, Volume 15, Issue 1, April 2002, Pages 1–15.

[64] Alison Sim, *The Tudor Housewife*, p. 22.

[65] Sir Nicholas Harris Nicolas, *Privy Purse Expenses of Elizabeth of York*, p. 78.

[66] Katherine French, "The Material Culture of Childbirth in Late Medieval London and its Suburbs", *Journal of Women's History*, Volume 28, Number 2, Summer 2016, pp. 126-148.

[67] Ibid.

[68] Geoffrey Parker, *Imprudent King: A New Life of Philip II*, p. 9.

[69] Christine Hallett, "The Attempt to Understand Puerperal Fever in the Eighteenth and Early Nineteenth Centuries: The Influence of Inflammation Theory", *Cambridge Journals Medical History*, 2005 Jan 1; 49(1): 1–28.

[70] Charles Wriothesley, *A Chronicle of England During the Reigns of the Tudors*, Volume 1, p. 5.

[71] Thomas R. Forbes, "The Regulation of English Midwives in the Sixteenth and Seventeenth Centuries", p. 237 in Philip K. Wilson (ed.) *Childbirth: The Medicalization of Obstetrics* (Taylor & Francis, 1996).

[72] For a full discussion of Jane Seymour's obstetrical history see Chapter 13.

[73] Audrey Eccles, *Obstetrics and Gynaecology in Tudor and Stuart England*, p. 113-115.

[74] BL, Egerton MS. 2713-2722, f. 16.

[75] Ibid.

[76] Sir Nicholas Harris Nicolas, *Privy Purse Expenses of Elizabeth of York*, pp. 62, 96.

[77] *Calendar of the Cecil Papers in Hatfield House*, Volume 11, entry for 20 March 1601.

[78] Sir Nicholas Harris Nicolas, *Privy Purse Expenses of Elizabeth of York*, p. 75.

[79] *CPR Henry VII 1485-1494*, p. 306.

[80] *Letters and Papers, Foreign and Domestic, Henry VIII*, Volume 12 Part 2, n. 923.

CHAPTER 4: "GENTLE AND FRUITFUL"

The story of the Tudor dynasty started with the thirteen-year-old Margaret Beaufort, Countess of Richmond, giving birth to her only son, Henry VII, on 28 January 1457. "It seemed a miracle that of so little a personage anyone should have been born at all", mused Margaret's confessor John Fisher many years later. Despite her young age, Margaret became a widow and a mother in quick succession. Her husband, Edmund Tudor, half brother of Henry VI, died in November 1456. Margaret never had any more children and wanted to protect her granddaughter and namesake from the perils of early childbirth, arguing that since Princess Margaret was not yet nine years old and was "so delicate and weak", the marriage had to be delayed for at least another nine years lest the King of Scots "would not wait, but injure her, and endanger her health".[1]

With the marriage of Henry VII to Elizabeth of York on 18 January 1486, England gained a new Queen. The majority of people in England believed that Elizabeth of York had a far better claim to the throne than her husband, "the unknown Welshman" who won the battle of Bosworth and toppled the last Yorkist King, Richard III. Yet Henry arranged his own coronation on 30 October 1485 to emphasise that he was the King in his own right and not because he was to marry the eldest daughter of Edward IV. In the late sixteenth century, Francis Bacon would sum up the feelings of many Englishmen, saying that Henry's victory at Bosworth gave him the knee of his subjects, but that his marriage to Elizabeth secured their hearts.

Henry VII had spent fourteen years in exile, and when he was crowned, observers noted that his mother, the formidable Lady Margaret Beaufort, Countess of Richmond, "wept marvellously" watching her son become King of England. These tears were fully justified. She had fought hard to see her son safely back in England, but she also knew that kings were easily toppled from their thrones, as illustrated by the example of Richard III. Henry's defeat of Richard was the beginning of a lifelong struggle to win the loyalty of his new, distrusting English subjects.

"He is disliked", wrote the Spanish envoy Pedro de Ayala in 1498.[2] Indeed, the ambassador observed that Henry wanted to rule "in the French fashion" but was unable to do so because the English were not used to such a model of kingship. To them, Henry was a foreigner brought up abroad and "not a great man". His wish to employ foreigners in his service reflected his suspicions about his English subjects, whose envy was, according to de Ayala, "diabolical" and "without equal".[3]

Elizabeth of York was the eldest child of Edward IV and his controversial bride, Elizabeth Woodville. Her birth on 11 February 1466 was widely celebrated at court and her mother's purification ceremony afterwards was a lavish affair. But although Elizabeth was a royal princess, her life was far from stable. After her father's death in April 1483, Elizabeth and her sisters were taken by their mother to the sanctuary at Westminster Abbey. Elizabeth Woodville feared the influence of her husband's brother, Richard, Duke of Gloucester, who intercepted Edward IV's eldest son, the young Edward V, on his way to London. Richard demanded that Elizabeth surrender her second son, whom she took to sanctuary, Richard, Duke of York. She parted with him very unwillingly and was soon to regret her decision.

Although Richard of Gloucester assured Elizabeth that her son Edward V would be crowned, he proclaimed him illegitimate and thus unfit to inherit. Richard proclaimed himself King of England and was crowned as

Richard III on 6 July 1483. Elizabeth Woodville's sons were seen "more rarely behind the bars and windows of the Tower", where they were placed, "until at length they ceased to appear altogether".[4] Richard III's first Parliament declared Elizabeth Woodville's marriage to Edward IV invalid due to Edward's earlier alleged pre-contract with another woman, and all of their children were thus deemed illegitimate. By March 1484, Richard reached out to his brother's widow and pledged that he would provide for her daughters and would arrange respectable marriages for all of them if they agreed to leave sanctuary. Elizabeth Woodville saw no other option but to trust the new King.

In December 1483, in the cathedral in Rennes, Henry Tudor swore an oath promising to marry Elizabeth of York and began planning an invasion of England. Henry naturally feared that unless he married Elizabeth or one of her sisters, large droves of his supporters would desert him. He was loath to admit later in his reign that many people rallied behind him because they wanted to see Edward IV's daughter on the throne. Writing in the late sixteenth century, Francis Bacon observed that Henry's "aversion towards the house of York was so predominant in him as it found place not only in his wars and councils, but in his chamber and bed". Bacon insinuated that Henry was not the most doting of husbands, adding: "And it is true that all his lifetime, while the Lady Elizabeth lived with him (for she died before him), he showed himself no very indulgent husband towards her, though she was beautiful, gentle and fruitful."[5]

It may be that rumours about Richard III's planned marriage to Elizabeth of York, which broke out in England and abroad in 1485, disheartened Henry and prejudiced him against Elizabeth. Indeed, Polydore Vergil, Henry VII's official and very first historian, affirmed that these rumours "pinched Henry by the very stomach" because he feared that his allies would forsake his cause if he failed to marry one of the daughters of Edward IV.[6] This suggests that Henry believed the rumours about Richard III's intended marriage to Elizabeth and assumed that Elizabeth was willing to marry her own uncle. At this point, the second eldest daughter of Edward IV, Cecily of York, was already married and the other York princesses were far too young to be espoused. Henry was so disheartened that he contemplated marrying Katherine Herbert, the daughter of his erstwhile guardian, but was convinced not to give up on his marriage to Elizabeth. On 30 March 1485 Richard III denied rumours that he had ever contemplated marrying his niece, and five months later he was slain by Henry Tudor at the battle of Bosworth.

After her marriage to Henry, Elizabeth of York quickly gained popularity as her father's heiress and became the embodiment of reconciliation. In creating the Tudor rose—a symbol of the two unified dynasties and an icon of the newly formed dynasty—Henry VII used Elizabeth's white rose of York and surrounded it with the outer petals of the red Lancastrian rose. Elizabeth, who was said to have been a "beautiful woman", had a milky-pale complexion, blue eyes and "yellow" hair. Much like her father, she had a tendency to become corpulent, but this can also be ascribed to her frequent pregnancies. Henry was described as "a man of body but lean and spare, albeit mighty and strong therewith, of personage and stature somewhat higher than the mean sort of men be, of a wonderful beauty and fair complexion, of countenance merry and smiling especially in his communication, his eyes grey, his teeth single, and hair thin".[7]

It was of paramount importance to the couple to beget offspring as soon as possible. Their first child, Prince Arthur, was born on 20 September 1486, eight months after the wedding took place. Some historians suggested that the boy was born prematurely, and the Queen's ill health after his birth strengthens this assertion. Elizabeth suffered from an attack of "ague". Just what this mysterious affliction was remains uncertain, "ague" being a catch-all term for all sorts of fevers. It's possible that the Queen experienced a difficult childbirth and, as her recent biographer pointed out, Elizabeth's "prolonged ill health after the birth of Prince Arthur may have been the reason why she did not conceive another child for nearly two and a half years".[8]

Five more children followed in quick succession: Margaret in 1489, Henry in 1491, Elizabeth in 1492, Mary in 1496 and Edmund in 1499. Shortly before Edmund's birth, the Spanish ambassador reported that "there had been much fear that the life of the Queen would be in danger, but the delivery, contrary to expectation, has been easy".[9] We do not know why there were fears for the Queen's life. It's likely that this judgment was formed based on Elizabeth's past deliveries. Or perhaps she experienced a difficult pregnancy.

In 1503, shortly before she gave birth to her last child, Elizabeth met with midwives, and it's likely that she had done so before every other delivery. A skilled midwife could determine a child's position in the womb by touching the woman's belly, and it's possible that Edmund's position caused great alarm and fears for the Queen's life in 1499.

His birth was greeted with joy: "The christening was very splendid, and the festivities such as though an heir to the Crown had been born."[10] Unfortunately, Edmund died in June 1500. Edmund wasn't the only child of Henry VII and Elizabeth of York who died during childhood. On 7 October 1495, the three-year-old Princess Elizabeth died at the royal nursery at Eltham Palace. The cause of her death remains unknown. The inscription on her tomb read: "Atropos, most merciless messenger of death, snatched her away". Reference to the ancient goddess Atropos led many historians over the centuries to an erroneous conclusion that the little princess died of "atrophy", wasting disease.[11]

Almost as soon as Henry and Elizabeth produced a male heir, the King started to look for a suitable bride for his firstborn son. In 1488, when Henry approached Isabella of Castile and Ferdinand of Aragon asking for their youngest daughter's hand in marriage, the Tudors were a new dynasty and Isabella was wary of risking her daughter's future, "bearing in mind what happens every day to the Kings of England". War over the succession had raged in England from 1460 to 1485, and there was no certainty that the Tudors would hold on to the throne, especially after a pretender to the Tudor throne, Perkin Warbeck, emerged in 1492 and gained international backing before he was finally captured in 1497. Surprisingly, he was not executed but placed at court, where he was allowed to mingle freely among the courtiers. Shortly after his capture, the Venetian ambassador reported that he had seen Perkin "in a chamber of the King's palace and habitation". "He is a well favoured young man, twenty-three years old, and his wife a very handsome woman", the ambassador observed, adding that "the King treats them well, but did not allow them to sleep together".

Henry VII's lenient treatment of Warbeck worried Katharine of Aragon's parents. They demanded that before Katharine's arrival, Henry should get rid of the two most powerful and potentially dangerous threats to his succession: Warbeck and Edward Plantagenet, Earl of Warwick, the son of George, Duke of Clarence. Ferdinand was heard saying that he would not send his daughter "to one who was not secure in his own kingdom". Henry VII hesitated; Warbeck, being a native of Tournai, was not his subject, and the King would probably have been content with perpetually locking him up in the Tower. Warwick constituted a different kind of threat. He was Edward IV's nephew, "the sole male descendant remaining in this branch of the family".[12] Many saw him as the rightful heir to the Yorkist throne, and people often used Warwick as a figurehead for rebellion. Henry VII decided that the establishment of his new dynasty was more important than the lives of Warbeck and Warwick, who were both executed in November 1499.

Thus Henry VII cleared the way for his heir's marriage to Katharine of Aragon—a marriage that the Spanish princess later declared had been "made in blood".[13] After the executions, the Spanish ambassador Rodrigo de Puebla exultantly reported to Ferdinand and Isabella that "there does not remain a drop of doubtful royal blood" in England except "the true blood of the King, the Queen and, above all, of the Prince of Wales".[14]

NOTES

[1] *Calendar of State Papers, Spain,* Volume 1, 210.
[2] *Calendar of State Papers, Spain,* Volume 1, 1485-1509, n. 209.
[3] Ibid.
[4] Dominic Mancini, *The Usurpation of Richard III*, p. 95.
[5] Francis Bacon, *Bacon: The History of the Reign of King Henry VII and Selected Works*, p. 20.
[6] *Three Books of Polydore Vergil's English History*, Volume 29, p. 215.
[7] Hall p. 504.
[8] Alison Weir, *Elizabeth of York: The First Tudor Queen*, p. 236.
[9] *Calendar of State Papers, Spain,* Volume 1, 1485-1509, n. 239.
[10] Ibid

[11] Alison Weir, *Elizabeth of York: The First Tudor Queen*, p. 309.
[12] John Edwards, *Archbishop Pole*, p. 272.
[13] Reginald Pole, *Pole's Defence of the Unity of the Church*, p. 197.
[14] *Calendar of State Papers, Spain,* Volume 1, n. 249.

CHAPTER 5: "THE MOST PITIFUL DISEASE"

The long anticipated marriage between Katharine of Aragon and Prince Arthur took place on 14 November 1501 at St Paul's Cathedral in London amid lavish celebrations and elaborately staged pageants. Later that evening the couple was ceremoniously put to bed in their nuptial chamber. The act of consummation of the marriage was not witnessed by the members of the court, and the wedding night itself would later become an issue weighed in court.[1] Henry VII sent Prince Arthur and Katharine of Aragon to Ludlow Castle in the Welsh Marches in December 1501, allowing the couple to live as man and wife, although he initially planned that Arthur "will know his wife sexually on the day of the wedding and then separate himself from her for two or three years because it is said that the prince is frail, and the King . . . wanted to have them [Arthur and Katharine of Aragon] with him for the first three years [of their marriage] so that the prince should mature in strength".[2] Yet, after consideration, the King was "unwilling to allow the prince and princess to be separated at any distance from each other", perhaps because he hoped they could conceive a child together.[3]

Unfortunately, Prince Arthur died on 2 April 1502, aged only sixteen, merely six months after marrying Katharine. Contemporary opinions vary as to the cause of his death. According to one source, Arthur died "of a malign vapour that proceeded from the constitution of their air". Andres Bernaldez, author of the chronicle of the reigns of Isabella of Castile and Ferdinand of Aragon, wrote that "Prince Arthur died of the plague a little while after his nuptials, being in the principality of Wales, in a place they call Pudlo (Ludlow). In this house was Donna Catalina left a widow, when she had been married scarcely six months".

The author of *The Receyt of the Lady Katherine*, an account of Katharine of Aragon's entry to London and her marriage to Arthur, described the young prince suffering "the most pitiful disease and sickness that with so sore and great violence had battled and driven in the singular parts of him inward; that cruel and fervent enemy of nature, the deadly corruption, did utterly vanquish and overcome the pure and friendfull blood, without all manner of physical help and remedy".[4]

These descriptions suggest that Arthur died of the plague or some other infectious disease. Katharine of Aragon fell ill at the same time, perhaps catching the same disease, but made a full recovery. However, some witnesses interviewed in the summer of 1529 as part of evidence-gathering for Henry VIII's annulment proceedings testified that Prince Arthur's health started to deteriorate much earlier than April. Lord St John remembered that "at Shrovetide [8 February 1502] after his [Arthur's] marriage, [he] began to decay, and was never so lusty in body and courage until his death".[5] Modern historians propose that Arthur died of the sweating sickness or suffered from pneumonia or consumption. The phrase "the singular parts of him inward" is also taken to mean that he had testicular cancer. Often when an otherwise healthy young individual, especially royal, died suddenly, the cause was ascribed to a surfeit of sexual activity. When Arthur died, at least one contemporary witness voiced a similar opinion, saying that Katharine "was the cause of the death of the most noble prince".[6]

In the 1530s, Katharine of Aragon's own physician, Dr Alcarez, said that Arthur "had been denied the strength necessary to know a woman, as if he was a cold piece of stone . . . because he was in the final stages of tisis".[7] "Tisis", or phthisis, was an illness known also as tuberculosis or consumption. During the reign of Katharine of Aragon's daughter with Henry VIII, reports were spread "that long before the death of Prince Arthur, he was known to be consumptive, and of so bad a constitution, that although they lived five months together, he had been unable to consummate marriage with her".[8] Symptoms of consumption included frequent and violent coughing, often with blood, but there's no evidence that Arthur was so severely ill.

Henry VII was at Greenwich Palace when his confessor informed him of Arthur's death. One of the King's heralds wrote: "When his Grace understood these sorrowful and heavy tidings, he sent for the Queen, saying that he and his Queen would take the painful sorrows together." Within the privacy of their apartments, the royal couple wept over the loss of their eldest son and heir. When the Queen consoled Henry after Arthur's death, she pointed out that Henry was his mother's only child and that they still had a son and two daughters left, adding, "God is still where he was, and we are both young enough [to have more children]".[9] These words indicate that, prompted by her eldest child's death, Elizabeth wanted to try to have another baby, preferably a son. She was soon pregnant again.

In November 1502, Elizabeth of York interviewed and rewarded a French wet nurse who visited her in Baynard's Castle, and another one, Mistress Harcourt, who conferred with the Queen at Westminster. She was actively preparing for childbirth, interviewing midwives and searching for a wet nurse who would breastfeed her child. On 26 January 1503, the Queen arrived in the Tower of London, where the royal couple intended to spend Candlemas, the Feast of the Purification of the Blessed Virgin Mary. On 2 February, the day of the feast, Elizabeth donned her royal robes and crown, attended Mass at the royal chapel and made her offering at the altar. Later that day she went into premature labour, giving birth to a daughter, Katherine, named either after her sister, who attended her in the Tower, or after Katharine of Aragon, Prince Arthur's widow. Alice Massey, the Queen's long-term midwife, attended the birth, as is evidenced by an entry in Elizabeth's Privy Purse accounts.

The Queen's health quickly deteriorated following Princess Katherine's birth. On 9 February, Henry VII summoned a physician from Plymouth to attend Elizabeth and two days later sent for the Queen's personal physician, Dr Hallysworth. But it was too late for Elizabeth: she died on 11 February 1503, her thirty-seventh birthday. Contemporaries agreed that she died "in childbed", as a result of premature birth.[10] Just what exactly caused her death is unknown. Nine days lapsed between Princess Katherine's birth on 2 February and the Queen's death on the 11th. Elizabeth may have experienced a postpartum haemorrhage. It's possible that excessive blood loss associated with premature labour was the direct cause of her death.

Plate 5: Funeral effigy of Elizabeth of York.

In total, Elizabeth of York was recorded to have given birth to seven children, four of whom lived at the time of her death. Polydore Vergil recorded that the Queen had "eight children, four boys and as many girls", and John Foxe repeated these numbers in the late sixteenth century.[11] It's been widely assumed by historians that before Princess Katherine's birth, Elizabeth had a son named George or Edward, but this view is not corroborated by existing evidence. When Prince Edmund died in June 1500, the Spanish ambassador remarked that he was the royal couple's "third son".[12] When Prince Arthur died on 2 April 1502, Elizabeth remarked that she and Henry still had "a fair prince and two fair princesses", referring to Henry, Margaret and Mary.[13] She became pregnant with Katherine around the end of May 1502, so a fourth son, if he ever existed, must have been born between June 1500 and May 1502 and died in infancy. Ambassadors and chroniclers didn't mention a fourth son. Elizabeth's recent biographer pointed out that a fourth son was unlikely to have existed because the St George altarpiece at Windsor, depicting the royal couple flanked by their children, shows four daughters and three sons. The painting dates from 1505-09, and another work of art dating from 1503 also shows three sons and four daughters.[14] Princess Katherine, Elizabeth of

York's last child, followed her mother to the grave shortly after birth.

NOTES

1 Read more in Chapter 8.
2 Frank Arthur, *The Youth of Henry VIII, A Narrative in Contemporary Letters*,pp. 24-25.
3 Ibid.
4 Alison Weir, *Elizabeth of York*, p. 391.
5 *Letters and Papers, Foreign and Domestic, Henry VIII*, Volume 4, n. 13.
6 Giles Tremlett's footnotes to *Catherine of Aragon: Henry's Spanish Wife*, consulted online, p. 18. https://www.faber.co.uk/9780571235124-catherine-of-aragon.html
7 Ibid.
8 *Calendar of State Papers, Venice*, Volume 5, n. 934.
9 Agnes Strickland, *Memoirs of the Queens of Henry VIII, and His Mother, Elizabeth of York*, p. 52.
10 Charles Wriothesley, *A Chronicle of England During the Reigns of the Tudors*, Volume 1, p. 5.
11 Alison Weir, *Elizabeth of York: The First Tudor Queen*, p. 309.
12 *Calendar of State Papers, Spain*, Volume 1, 1485-1509, n. 268.
13 Agnes Strickland, op.cit.
14 Alison Weir, *Elizabeth of York: The First Tudor Queen*, p. 333.

CHAPTER 6: "OF TENDER AND FEEBLE NATURE"

Elizabeth of York's death had a dramatic impact on the life of her only surviving son, Henry, Prince of Wales. Elizabeth was the embodiment of every quality Henry would value in a woman in his later life; she was obedient, kind, gentle, loving and fruitful. Many years later, when he was married to his sixth wife, Henry would praise his late mother, saying that she was "as good and as virtuous a woman as ever lived in this world".[1] To him, she was always his "dearest mother" whose death was a "hateful intelligence", in his own words.[2] An illumination in a contemporaneous manuscript, *The Vaux Passional*, at the National Library of Wales shows the young Prince Henry clad in black, kneeling and weeping by his mother's empty bed.[3]

In a touching eulogy written after Elizabeth of York's death, Thomas More wrote that Henry VII was now expected to fulfil the role of both father and mother to his children, "now must ye supply the mother's part also".[4]

Henry was forty-six and father to three children: Prince Henry, his successor, and Princesses Margaret and Mary. Margaret, the King's favourite child, left to marry James IV of Scotland shortly after Elizabeth's death.

Henry VII was not young by the standards of his epoch, but he could still father children, although shortly after Elizabeth of York's death he was said to have been "a weak man and sickly, not likely to be a long-lived man".[5] Henry appeared much older than his forty-six years merited, with "teeth few, poor and blackish", thinning grey hair and failing eyesight.[6] Having just one male heir was risky, considering the perils of everyday life.

Of the three sons he had with Elizabeth of York, only one was still alive. Prince Henry, twelve at the time of his mother's death, was a healthy and robust boy with a ruddy complexion and red hair. Tall and strong, he looked nothing like his ageing father, resembling his maternal grandfather, the tall and muscular Edward IV. Many years later, Henry's enemies would say that his father "had no affection nor fancy unto him", perhaps because of young Henry's resemblance of his Plantagenet grandfather.[7]

The Spanish ambassador Fuensalida recorded that Henry VII kept his only son "locked up like a lady".[8] The young prince lived in a chamber which could only be accessed through the King's suite and was accompanied everywhere by a selected group of servants. Henry was "so subjugated that he does not speak a word except when he answers the King's questions".[9] Henry VII's treatment of his heir stemmed from a suspicious mind. He wasn't popular among his subjects, and Elizabeth of York's death laid him open to the machinations of people who perceived him as a usurper. Having gained the crown on the battlefield, Henry always feared that he would end up like Richard III, killed and betrayed by his own nobles.

In 1499, he asked a Welsh priest who foretold the deaths of Edward IV and Richard III "to tell him in what manner his latter end would come". The priest "told the King that his life would be in great danger during the whole year, and informed him, in addition to many other unpleasant things, that there are two parties of very different political creeds in his kingdom".[10] Although Henry forbade the priest to talk to others about this unfavourable prophecy, the news spread, and by 1503 it was well-known in England that there existed a prophecy according to which Henry VII wouldn't reign longer than Edward IV.[11]

The tale of two factions with different political agendas wasn't that far from the truth: one party supported Henry VII's heir while the other was eager to see a Plantagenet on the throne again. When in 1504 the possibility of Henry VII's death was discussed by the King's officials in Calais, "my lord prince" was not even mentioned, whereas Edmund de la Pole and Edward Stafford, Duke of Buckingham, were said to have been likely successors.[12]

Although clearly in poor health, Henry decided to remarry, hoping to beget more sons and build an international alliance. His first choice fell upon Katharine of Aragon, his late son's virgin widow, who was still residing in England. Isabella of Castile, however, forbade such a union, thundering in one of the letters to her ambassador that "merely to have spoken of it is offensive to the ears, and we will not agree to it for anything in the world".[13] Henry VII was eager to maintain the Anglo-Spanish alliance and agreed to a marriage between Katharine and Prince Henry instead. But the King didn't give up on remarriage.

In 1505, he considered marrying Joanna of Naples, Ferdinand of Aragon's niece. Born in 1479, Joanna was the widow of King Ferdinand II of Naples, whom she had married at seventeen. Although the marriage was childless, Joanna's hand was used as a bargaining tool on the international marriage market by Ferdinand of Aragon and Isabella of Castile.

Marrying someone unknown posed a question of compatibility and the ability to feel physical attraction. In December 1504, Henry VII told the Spanish ambassador Rodrigo de Puebla that "it would not seem the right or honest thing" to conclude the marriage negotiations without a detailed report concerning "the person and appearance" of Joanna of Naples. If Joanna "was ugly and not beautiful and well-proportioned, the King of England would not take or dare to take her in exchange for any treasure, considering the English are like that."[14]

Henry VII's instructions for his ambassadors regarding Joanna of Naples's appearance are still extant and provide a vivid glimpse into the King's mind-set. They were to engage Joanna in lively conversations and "approach as near to her mouth as they honestly may, to the intent that they may feel the condition of her breath, whether it be sweet or not, and to mark at every time when they speak with her if they feel any savour of spices, rose-water, or musk by the breath of her mouth". The ambassadors were also instructed to pay attention to Joanna's height and feet: How tall was she, and was she wearing any platform shoes designed to make her appear taller than she truly was? The most important instructions concerned Joanna's face and body:

"To mark and note well the age and stature of the said young queen, and the features of her body, the favour of her visage, the clearness of her skin, the colours of her hair, to note well her eyes, brows, teeth, and lips, to mark well the fashion of her nose, especially to note her complexion, her arms, hands, fingers, neck, whether she have any sickness, deformity, or blemish, to mark her breasts and paps, whether they be big or small, and to mark whether there appear any hair about her lips or not."

The ambassadors observed Joanna of Naples carefully and sent a satisfactory report to the King. The twenty-six-year-old Dowager Queen of Naples was of middle stature, with brown hair, "her eyes of a colour brown, somewhat greyish; her complexion very fair, sanguine and clean". Her lips were "somewhat round and thick, according to the proportion of her visage", with no hair and no foul smells emanating from her mouth. Her nose was "a little rising in the midward, and a little coming or bowing towards the end". As to Joanna's body, her arms were "somewhat round and not very small". Her hands, seen by the ambassadors from up close when they bowed to kiss them on three occasions, were "somewhat fully and soft, and fair and clean skinned". Joanna's neck was "fully and comely, and not misshapen, nor very short nor long, but meetly, after the proportion of her personage". Her breasts were "fully and somewhat big". Italian fashion favoured low-cut décolletages and corsets that pushed the breasts upwards, hence the ambassadors' comment:

> "The said queen's breasts be somewhat great and fully, and inasmuch as they were trussed somewhat high, after the manner of the country, the which causeth her grace to seem much more fuller, and her neck to be shorter."[15]

Henry VII also considered marrying Archduchess Margaret of Savoy, the daughter of Holy Roman Emperor Maximilian. In August 1505, two portraits of Margaret were delivered to Henry VII; when Katharine of Aragon saw them, she opined that they were not the best likenesses of Margaret and that the Estonian artist Michael Sittow would have done a better job.[16] Margaret, who was married twice before, was twenty-five, and although she was never a great beauty, with her prominent Habsburg jaw and thick, half-opened lips, she was at least known to have been fertile, having had a miscarriage in 1497.

The only problem with Margaret was that she had no inclination to remarry. As a child, she was promised to Charles VII of France but was jilted when Charles took Anne of Brittany as his bride. Then in 1496, she married the son and heir of Isabella of Castile. However, John, Prince of Asturias, died shortly after the wedding. Margaret's third marriage, to Philibert of Savoy, was by all accounts a harmonious one, but the young duke died in his early twenties, leaving Margaret a widow yet again. Henry VII knew that Margaret didn't want to marry, and a clause in the Anglo-Imperial treaty stated that Maximilian was "further bound to use all his paternal influence over the Archduchess Margaret in order to persuade her to consent to this marriage".[17]

Portrait exchange was an important part of courtship rituals, and in October 1505 Henry VII ordered his own likeness to be sent to Margaret. The painting shows Henry VII wearing a black cap and dressed in a sumptuous red-and-gold brocade surcoat trimmed with white fur worn over a black tunic. Margaret kept this portrait in her collection, a reminder of the marriage that never came to fruition.

Another woman whom Henry VII considered as a potential bride was Joanna of Castile, the elder sister of

Katharine of Aragon. Isabella of Castile's death in November 1504 changed Joanna's rank from Princess of Asturias to Queen of Castile. When her husband, Philip the Handsome, died in September 1506, Joanna was a queen with no king by her side. Her sanity was questioned by her husband and father, who fought for dominance in Castile after Queen Isabella's death, but Henry VII apparently saw no problem with Joanna's mental health. Henry met Joanna and Philip when their ship was wrecked off the coast of England in 1506 and proclaimed that she seemed "very well" to him "and although her husband and those who came with him depicted her as crazy, I did not see her as other than sane".[18] This marriage also came to nothing.

Isabella of Castile's death changed the way Henry VII looked at Katharine of Aragon. She was merely a daughter of Ferdinand of Aragon, and not a great heiress like her sister Joanna. In June 1505, Prince Henry, instructed by his father, renounced his betrothal to Katharine. Henry VII was tired of Ferdinand of Aragon's repeated failure to send the remaining portion of her dowry. The year 1505 marked the turning point in Henry VII's relationship with his former daughter-in-law. Living on scraps of Henry's charity, Katharine incurred debts that she couldn't afford to pay. "I am in the greatest trouble and anguish in the world", she wrote in one of her numerous letters to Ferdinand of Aragon. Not only was she "all but naked", lacking new clothes, but she was also unable to pay wages and marriage portions for her servants.[19]

In addition to her financial troubles, Katharine's health was a cause for concern. Separation from her family and homeland provoked a physical reaction in the form of fever when she left Spain in 1501.[20] The first serious illness occurred in 1504, when Katharine "had been unwell for three days, suffering from ague and derangement of the stomach". She initially recovered after Henry VII allowed her to visit Greenwich, a pleasure palace on the Thames. But after a week spent recuperating there, Katharine fell ill again, "and much more seriously than before". The Spanish ambassador related:

"Before she had recovered, King Henry was obliged to leave on a visit to Kent. The Princess of Wales then returned to the house in which she had formerly lived. She had, however, not improved. She is rather worse, for she now suffers every day from cold and heat. The illness seems sometimes serious, for the Princess has no appetite, and her complexion has changed entirely. Nevertheless, the physicians have much confidence, and say that the patient will soon recover. The first attack of ague began four weeks ago. The Princess has had at intervals a bad cold and cough since then. The physicians have twice purged her, and twice attempted to bleed her; but no blood came. It is difficult to say whether it was the fault of the man who bled her. He is the licentiate who resides with the Princess as her physician, and he generally bleeds very well. She desires, very much, that the operation be repeated, being persuaded that if she were bled she would be well directly. The physicians, however, delay the bleeding, and purge her."[21]

The letters Katharine exchanged with her father offer a glimpse into her medical record. Following Prince Henry's repudiation of their betrothal, Katharine's health worsened significantly. In 1505, she complained: "I have had so much pain and annoyance that I have lost my health in a great measure so that for two months I have had severe tertian fevers, and this will be the cause that I shall soon die."[22] Tudor doctors categorised fevers according to when they appeared and how long they lasted: a quotidian fever (attacked daily) in winter, a tertian (recurring every three days) in spring or summer and quartan (every fourth day) in the fall. "Tertian fever" implied malaria. In April 1506, Katharine informed her father that she was in desperate need of a new confessor because for six months she had been "near death".[23] Henry VII took Katharine's illnesses seriously and sent his Genoese physician to treat her. Katharine was very grateful, writing to her father that "I am so much beholden to him that I know not wherewith to pay him, for that (after God) he gave me my life in a great sickness that I had".[24] In 1508, the Spanish ambassador Don Gutierre Gómez de Fuensalida was concerned that Katharine might "fall into some great illness" because "her grace isn't healthy, but is thin and very discoloured and her complexion is much damaged".[25]

Katharine's troubles would continue, and only Henry VII's worsening health could save her. Henry VII's health started to decline around 1503. Polydore Vergil, Henry's sixteenth-century biographer, recorded:

"For in the following three years of his life, thrice about springtime he fell ill, was greatly incapacitated, his bodily strength declining by degrees. This progressive ill-health he could not endure without a corresponding mental decline until in his third illness he clearly recognised that he was going to die."[26]

Vergil's testimony is confirmed by other sources. In 1507, the Spanish ambassador reported that Henry had a "severe illness" that kept him confined to his private chambers. "The quinsy had prevented him for six days from eating and drinking" and Henry's "life was despaired of".[27] Although he rallied, from February to March 1508 Henry was confined to his apartments again, suffering an attack of debilitating gout. Spanish ambassador Gutierre Gomez de Fuensalida wrote that his audience with the King had to be postponed "because his health was not good, that it was mainly his foot that was unwell, where gout had spread, and that when he was ready to talk to me, he would let me know".[28] When Henry's gout was not showing any signs of improving, he sent word to Fuensalida that "although he did not completely recover from his illness and he was not ready to talk about business, he could not wait to see and hear me out". Finally, on 4 March 1508, Fuensalida saw the King but was informed that Henry was "not well and he would like your speech to be brief".[29]

In July 1508, the King was said to have been "in the last stage of consumption" and not likely to live long.[30] By March 1509, rumours circulated abroad that "the King of England was very ill and utterly without hope of recovery".[31] Yet even his ill-health didn't soften Henry's attitude towards his daughter-in-law. In March 1509, Katharine complained in yet another pitiful letter to her father:

"To tell the truth, my necessities have risen so high that I do not know how to maintain myself. For I have already sold my household goods, as it was impossible to avoid it, and I do not know whence I can have anything else. Some days ago, speaking with the King about my wants, he said to me, that he was not bound to give my servants food, or even to my own self, but that the love he bore me would not allow him to do otherwise. From this your Highness will see to what a state I am reduced, when I am warned that even my food is given me almost as alms."

Katharine then added ominously:

"I am afraid I might do something which neither the King of England nor your Highness, who has much more weight, would be able to prevent, unless, and that is necessary, you send for me so that I may conclude my few remaining days in serving God."[32]

Tensions within her own household as well as Henry VII's mistreatment drove Katharine to the brink. "Things here become daily worse, and my life more and more insupportable", she complained, "I can no longer bear this in any manner."[33] Was Katharine hinting she could commit suicide? She was trapped in England, neither wife nor mother, in a state of limbo. But then, in April 1509, all was to change, for Henry VII was on his deathbed.

Bishop John Fisher, Margaret Beaufort's chaplain and confessor, described Henry VII's last moments in great detail. The fifty-two-year-old King died in his bedchamber after receiving sacraments, with his gaze piously fixed onto a crucifix held out before him. Lying in his bed and "continually abiding the sharp assaults of death" for twenty-seven agonising hours, Henry "with all his might and power cried upon the name of our lord" before he passed away on 21 April 1509.[34] A drawing by Garter King of Arms Thomas Wriothesley, currently preserved in the British Library, shows Henry VII dying in his richly ornamented four-poster bed, surrounded by his most intimate courtiers and household officers. Also present are two clerics and three physicians holding flasks with the King's urine.[35]

Yet an overlooked primary source shows that Henry VII did not die in his bed.[36] A manuscript in the British Library contains a description of "the manner of the removing of the King's corpse from his oratory or secret closet to his chapel" at Richmond Palace.[37] According to Wriothesley, Henry VII's death was "secretly kept by the space of two days" and announced officially at court on 23 April.[38] The delay in announcing the King's death is usually said to have occurred to allow time to orchestrate the arrests of Empson and Dudley, Henry's two unpopular ministers. Could it be that the delay was also caused by the *manner* of Henry VII's death? He died in his private oratory, suggesting a sudden collapse. Fisher's elaborate account of the King's last hours as well as Wriothesley's drawing were most likely attempts to promote the idea of "an exemplary death".[39] Fisher's and Wriothesley's dramatic accounts are thus proven to be fabrications aiming at depicting a glorious and godly ending of the King who had invaded England twenty-four years earlier.

According to two travellers who visited Richmond Palace in 1599, the King left instructions that his intestines were to be removed and "slung full of blood against the walls of a chamber in the palace, as a symbol that he conquered the kingdom by force, slaying Richard III who had usurped the realm, in battle". No other source corroborates this, but the men asserted that "many traces of blood were pointed out to us in one room".[40] If this is indeed true, then Henry VII died as he lived—proud of conquering England in 1485.

Plate 6: Funeral effigy of Henry VII.

NOTES

[1] *State Papers,* Volume 11, p. 229.
[2] Marie Louise Bruce, *The Making of Henry VIII*, p. 192.
[3] *The Vaux Passional*, Peniarth MS 482D, f. 9 r.
[4] Agnes Strickland, *Lives of the Queens of England*, Volume 2, p. 59.
[5] *Letters and Papers Illustrative of the Reigns of Richard III and Henry VII*, Volume 1, p. 233.
[6] For comments about the King's teeth and hair, see Polydore Vergil, *The Anglica Historia*. Henry mentioned his failing eyesight in a letter to his mother: "Madam, my sight is nothing so perfect as it has been", quoted in *Life of Margaret Beaufort* by C. A. Halsted, p. 211.
[7] *Letters and Papers, Foreign and Domestic, Henry VIII,* Volume 13 Part 2, n. 804 (7).

[8] *Correspondencia de Gutierre Gomez de Fuensalida*, p. 449.
[9] Ibid.
[10] *Calendar of State Papers, Spain,* Volume 1, n. 239.
[11] *Letters and Papers Illustrative of the Reigns of Richard III and Henry VII*, Volume 1, p. 236.
[12] Ibid., p. 233.
[13] *Calendar of State Papers, Spain,* Volume 1, n. 360.
[14] Jose Maria Doussinague, *Fernando el Católico y Germana de Foix: Un Matrimonio por Razón de Estado*, p. 248.
[15] George Gordon Coulton, *Life in the Middle Ages*, p. 160.
[16] *Calendar of State Papers, Spain,* Volume 1, n. 439.
[17] Ibid., n. 455.
[18] Bethany Aram, *Juana the Mad*, p. 83.
[19] Anne Crawford, *Letters of the Queens of England, 1100-1547*, p. 168.
[20] *Calendar of State Papers, Spain*, Volume 1, 1485-1509, n. 296.
[21] Ibid., n. 398.
[22] Mary Ann Everett Green, *Letters of Royal and Illustrious Ladies of Great Britain*, Volume 1, p. 133.
[23] Ibid., p. 140.
[24] Ibid., p. 142.
[25] *Correspondencia de Gutierre Gomez de Fuensalida*, p. 435.
[26] Polydore Vergil, *The Anglica Historia of Polydore Vergil, A.D. 1485-1537*, p. 143.
[27] *Calendar of State Papers, Spain,* Volume 1, n. 511.
[28] *Correspondencia de Gutierre Gomez de Fuensalida*, pp. 414-415.
[29] Ibid., p. 416.
[30] *Calendar of State Papers, Spain,* Volume 1, n. 586.
[31] *Calendar of State Papers Relating To English Affairs in the Archives of Venice,* Volume 1, 1202-1509, n. 939.
[32] *Calendar of State Papers, Spain,* Supplement To Volumes 1 and 2, n. 3.
[33] Ibid.
[34] *The English Works of John Fisher: Bishop of Rochester*, p. 273-277.
[35] BL Add MS 45131, f. 54. https://www.bl.uk/collection-items/henry-vii-on-his-deathbed
[36] I'm grateful to Ian Coulson for bringing this source to my attention.
[37] BL, Arundel MS 26, f. 28.
[38] S. J. Gunn, "The Accession of Henry VIII", *Institute of Historical Research*, Volume 64, Issue 155, (October 1991), pp. 278-288.
[39] Thomas Penn, *Winter King*, p. 314.
[40] P. E. Razzell (ed.), *The Journals of Two Travellers in Elizabethan and Early Stuart England*, p. 100.

CHAPTER 7: "SONS WILL FOLLOW"

Henry VII was succeeded by his son. The new King Henry VIII decided to marry Katharine of Aragon, saying it was his dying father's last wish. It's more likely, however, that the young King fell in love with Katharine. In a letter to Katharine's former sister-in-law, Archduchess Margaret of Savoy, he confessed that "even if we were still free, it is she, nevertheless, that we would choose for our wife before all other".[1]

The fact that Katharine used to be his late brother's wife did not bother Henry much, or at least not yet. Although six years older than him—she was twenty-three to his seventeen—Katharine was young, beautiful and vivacious. In the words of up-and-coming courtier Thomas More, she possessed "all those qualities that make for beauty in a very charming young girl"; Henry clearly agreed because he wanted no other bride but her.[2]

Katharine became pregnant for the first time shortly after the wedding that took place in June 1509. The first hint of her pregnancy comes from Henry VIII's letter to

Katharine's father, Ferdinand of Aragon, in November 1509: "Your daughter, our dearest consort, has conceived in her womb a living child, and is right heavy therewith, which we signify to your Majesty for the great joy thereof that we take, and the exultation of our whole realm."[3]

Katharine's pregnancy was no longer a secret, and her large belly with the moving child inside it proclaimed the Queen's fertility to the entire world. Ferdinand took a keen interest in his daughter's condition, writing back to her on 28 November that "her pregnancy is a great blessing since she, her husband, and the English people have wished it so much". "May God give you a good delivery", he said conventionally, referring to the imminent childbirth. Ferdinand vowed that he "will continually pray the Almighty to grant his prayers till he is informed that she has given birth to her child". Apart from referring to the religious dimension of childbirth, Ferdinand added some practical advice to Katharine, begging her "to be careful of her health". Ferdinand warned Katharine that "during her pregnancy she must avoid all exertion, and especially not write with her own hand", adding that "with the first child it is requisite for women to take more care of themselves than is necessary in subsequent pregnancies".[4]

On 31 January 1510, Katharine "brought forth prematurely a daughter, without any other pain except that one knee pained her the night before". "This affair was so secret", wrote Katharine's confessor Friar Diego Fernandez, "that no one knew it until now, except the King my Lord, two Spanish women, a physician and I".[5] But this was not the end of the matter. In fact, Friar Diego's letter was written in May 1510, four months after the events that he described. Katharine, friar Diego affirmed, wanted to conceal the loss of her daughter from the world—and from the King—and had convinced herself that she was still pregnant because "her belly was so distended as I've never seen in a pregnant woman". "The physician said that Her Highness remained pregnant of another child, and it was believed and kept secret". Katharine apparently believed that despite the premature birth of a stillborn daughter, she was still pregnant, perhaps with a twin. The premature birth of a baby girl was kept secret, and Katharine carried on with the hope that she was still with child.

Preparations for the birth of a royal baby were in full swing when in February 1510 Sir Andrew Windsor, Keeper of the Great Wardrobe, received a warrant from Henry VIII "for the use of our nursery, God willing". The elaborate "cradle of estate" for the infant was to be covered with crimson cloth of gold. There were provisions for pillows, sheets and swaddling bands for the baby as well as beds and linen for "mistress Nurse", the wet nurse who would breastfeed the child, two rockers who would keep watch over the royal baby's cradle and Lady Mistress, who had her chamber fitted with heavy hangings to ward off droughts.[6]

In March 1510, Katharine ceremoniously "took to her chamber" to await the birth of her child. Yet there was no birth, and the swelling of her belly decreased. Ambassador Luis Caroz thundered in a letter to Ferdinand of Aragon that "it was a folly to affirm that a menstruating woman was pregnant", referring to the fact that Katharine experienced bleeding five months after her pregnancy was made public.[7] Katharine remained confined to her chambers until May, when it became apparent that she would not give birth anytime soon. Shortly before Friar Diego wrote the whole account of Katharine's pregnancy to Ferdinand of Aragon on 25 May, Katharine was forced to tell Henry VIII that she had given birth prematurely to a baby girl in January and was assured by her physician that she remained pregnant with another baby despite the stillbirth.

But Katharine didn't want to admit the defeat and informed Friar Diego that she believed she was three months pregnant. This would mean that she had sexual relations with the King in February 1510, when they both believed she was still pregnant. Sex during pregnancy was forbidden, and the fact that the royal couple engaged in intimacy at that point testifies to how much in love they must have been at the time. Katharine was careful not to reveal the news of this new pregnancy to anyone except Friar Diego. "This your Highness is to believe, for it is as true as I am a man", the friar affirmed to Ferdinand of Aragon. He added further:

"Her Highness denies it to all the world and to the King, but to me she has said it that she is since three months [pregnant], and her Highness told me also that her belly had since swollen greatly; her Highness cannot deny it because she is already, by the grace of our Lord, very large, so much so that all the physicians know and affirm it, and a Spanish woman who is in her private chamber told me the same thing from secret signs which they have."[8]

On 27 May 1510, the Queen wrote to her father informing him laconically that "some days before she was delivered of a daughter". Katharine didn't tell Ferdinand the truth; in her version of events, she gave birth to a stillborn girl in May, not in January, and she didn't mention that she had taken to her chamber in March, two months after the stillbirth. She added further that stillbirth was considered an ill omen in England and begged Ferdinand "not to be angry with her" for losing a baby because it was "the will of God".[9] Deep down Katharine suffered, was "sad and disconsolate" and confided in Friar Diego that "she had desired to gladden the King and the people with a prince".[10]

What Katharine did not know was that her father had been informed about her pregnancy and its outcome by two sources: Ambassador Luis Caroz and confessor Diego Fernandez. Ambassador Caroz reported that Henry VIII's councillors believed that since the Queen was not pregnant she may have been barren. He added further that although Katharine was in good health—"the Queen has a pretty and most healthy colour in her face"—he believed that "some irregularity in her eating and the food which she eats cause her some indisposition, the consequence of which is that she does not menstruate well". The consequence of Katharine's irregular menstruations was, according to Caroz, the reason why Katharine couldn't conceive.

Katharine was not mistaken about her condition. In May 1510, as she still lived away from the public glare, she was indeed pregnant, although she was careful not to announce it publicly until she was absolutely certain about her condition. Louis Caroz wrote that "she wishes to wait until this pregnancy is well certified in the third month, so that the good news may temper the annoyance of his Highness at what had passed".[11] On 1 January 1511, she gave birth to a baby boy who was named Henry, after his father. The royal infant was christened on 5 January in the presence of the ambassadors of the pope, France, Spain and Venice. Katharine was recovering well, and her wish to give England a prince had come true.

On 22 February 1511, tragedy struck: the infant prince died. Katharine was devastated and "like a natural woman, made much lamentation", whereas the King "like a wise prince, took this dolorous chance wondrous wisely and, the more to comfort the Queen, he made no great mourning outwardly".[12] Yet everyone at court knew that the death of his firstborn son shook Henry VIII to the core, for the French ambassador informed his colleague that "Winchester and the Council advise him not to present the King's letter touching the death of the Prince or say a word about it at present, as it would only revive their King's grief".[13]

On 30 September 1511, Cardinal Wolsey wrote that "the Queen is thought to be with child", but nothing further was heard about her condition.[14] In October 1513, Katharine gave birth to a son, as reported by the Venetian ambassador.[15] The year 1513 marked Katharine's success as regent during Henry VIII's absence on a war campaign in France. In September 1513, when England was invaded by the Scottish King James IV, English armies led by Thomas Howard won a spectacular victory. The birth of a son during such a time was Katharine's success, but not for long, for this infant died shortly after birth. Another son was born to Katharine and Henry in November 1514. According to the Venetian ambassador, "the Queen has been delivered of a stillborn male child of eight months to the very great grief of the whole court".[16] The first rumours of a possible divorce between Henry and Katharine were passed within the ambassadorial circles in 1514, but the idea didn't come to fruition at that time.

In January 1516, Henry VIII wrote jocularly to his rival, Francis I of France, that Katharine was pregnant again and advised that Francis "should put Queen Claude in the like situation".[17] On 18 February 1516, Katharine gave birth to a baby girl who was christened Mary in a lavish ceremony three days later. When the Venetian ambassador visited the King to congratulate him "on the birth of his daughter and the well-being of the Queen", he expressed the sentiment that Venice "would have been yet more pleased had the child been a son". Henry thanked the ambassador and said: "We are both young; if it was a daughter this time, by the grace of God the sons will follow."[18] Henry had no reason to doubt that he would have sons with Katharine; she was thirty-one and clearly very fertile, whereas at twenty-five Henry was in his prime.

Henry's lack of a male heir was further highlighted when his younger sister, Mary, only nineteen years old at the time, gave birth to her first child, a son she named Henry, after her royal brother, on 11 March 1516.[19] She would produce more children, including another son in the 1520s. The King's elder sister, Margaret, Dowager Queen of Scots, already had a healthy son who was now king, James V, born in 1512, and a daughter born in October 1515. Until he had sons of his own, Henry's nephews were perceived as plausible candidates to the throne.

Yet the sons Henry hoped for never came. Katharine of Aragon's last recorded childbirth took place on 9 November 1518 when she was delivered of a stillborn daughter in the eighth month of pregnancy. This time Henry

VIII was not the only one devastated because "never had the kingdom so anxiously desired anything as it did a prince".[20] Katharine's loss came when Princess Mary was betrothed to the French Dauphin Francis. Had Henry VIII known what the outcome of this pregnancy would be, he would never have allowed for Princess Mary's French match because, as Sebastiano Giustinian reported, "the sole fear of this kingdom" was "that it may pass into the power of the French through this marriage".[21] Ultimately, Princess Mary was the only child of Katharine of Aragon and Henry VIII who survived the perils of early childhood and lived to adulthood, eventually attaining the crown as England's first Queen Regnant in 1553.

It has been claimed by several historians that Katharine of Aragon experienced frequent miscarriages, but her childbearing history clearly shows that this is not the case. By definition, miscarriage occurs when a foetus dies during the first twenty weeks (around the fifth month) of pregnancy.[22] Stillbirth is typically defined as foetal death at or after twenty or twenty-eight weeks of pregnancy. There is not a single example of a miscarriage in Katharine's obstetrical history, unless the pregnancy reported by Wolsey in 1511 ended in miscarriage—although it's equally possible that this pregnancy was a mere rumour. It's more accurate to say that Katharine experienced frequent stillbirths, as she usually gave birth prematurely, usually around the eighth month of pregnancy. Recent theory as to why Katharine experienced so many stillbirths suggests that Henry VIII may have had the rare Kell-positive blood type, which causes miscarriages, stillbirths and neonatal deaths if the mother has Kell-negative blood type.[23]

It's been recently suggested that in her youth Katharine may have suffered from anorexia nervosa.[24] This is based on two pieces of evidence. In 1510, the Spanish ambassador recorded that "some irregularity in her eating and the food which she eats cause her some indisposition, the consequence of which is that she does not menstruate well".[25] The second piece of evidence is the papal bull granted to Henry VIII, wherein Pope Julius II gave Henry the authority to restrain Katharine from excessive religious observances such as rigorous fasting that could, it was feared, impair Katharine's ability to bear children.[26] Whether Katharine truly suffered from anorexia in her youth is open to debate. She certainly gained weight as she aged, often being described as corpulent.

Frequent childbearing and the losses of her children took their toll on Katharine of Aragon's appearance. In

1515, when she was thirty, one of the Venetian ambassadors remarked that "the Queen is rather ugly than otherwise", contrasting her worn-out appearance with the attractive looks of her young ladies-in-waiting.[27] In 1519, Francis I quipped that Henry VIII "has an old deformed wife, while he himself is young and handsome".[28] It is generally assumed that the French King was referring to Katharine's corpulent figure; several years later one eyewitness described her as "of low stature" and "rather stout".[29] Yet there's evidence that Francis was referring not only to Katharine's bulky figure but also to a deformity of her jaw—a deformity that has been overlooked by modern historians until now.

In the vast collections of the Victoria & Albert Museum in London, there is a boxwood draughtsman that bears a portrait of Katharine of Aragon, dating to c. 1535.[30] She is depicted in profile to the left, with her head covered by a hood of English making, and wears a dress with a low-cut décolletage that emphasises her ample bosom. Around her neck, she wears a chain with a pendant. The feature that draws the viewer's attention is the half-opened, jutting jaw. This is not the only depiction of Katharine with a pronounced jaw. The Kunsthistorisches Museum in Vienna holds a set of twenty-seven boxwood-on-walnut game pieces, dating to c. 1535, depicting various historical personages of the sixteenth century.[31] Katharine of Aragon is one of them: She is depicted wearing similar headdress, clothes and pendant as in the Victoria & Albert boxwood draughtsman but faces the viewer with her eyes turned to the left. Like in the Victoria & Albert piece, her jaw is half-opened and pronounced. The National Portrait Gallery in London preserves a miniature of Katharine, dating to c. 1525-26, wherein her jaw is more pronounced that in other known portraits.[32] Finally, the Museum of Fine Arts in Boston has a portrait of the Queen wherein her jaw is closed but clearly jutting.[33]

Plate 7: Author's sketch of the boxwood draughtsman depicting Katharine of Aragon. The original is preserved in the Victoria & Albert Museum, London.

The abovementioned evidence suggests that Katharine of Aragon suffered from mandibular prognathism, much like her Habsburg nephew Charles V (Katharine's sister Joanna married into the Habsburg dynasty in 1496, espousing Philip the Handsome, Duke of Burgundy). The so called "Habsburg jaw" refers to the inherited trait which was present and clearly evident in the Habsburg family, Maximilian I and Charles V being the most prominent examples in the sixteenth century. This condition manifests itself as a jutting of the jaw. Yet the Habsburgs were not the only ones who suffered from prognathism. The Trastámara dynasty, from which both of Katharine's parents descended, had several members who suffered from prognathism. Katharine's half uncle, Henry IV of Castile, was the most prominent example, as evidenced by his skeletal remains. John II of Castile, Katharine's maternal grandfather, also suffered from prognathism, as did the first Trastámara King of Castile, Henry II. Clearly, prognathism ran in Katharine of Aragon's family and was a trait she inherited.

NOTES

[1] *Letters and Papers, Foreign and Domestic, Henry VIII,* Volume 1, n. 119.
[2] Giles Tremlett, *Catherine of Aragon: Henry's Spanish Queen*, p. 83.

[3] Muriel St Clare Byrne, *The Letters: A Selection, with a Few Other Documents*, p. 12.
[4] *Calendar of State Papers, Spain,* Volume 2, 1509-1525, n. 28.
[5] *Calendar of State Papers, Spain,* Supplement To Volumes 1 and 2, n. 7.
[6] *Letters and Papers, Foreign and Domestic, Henry VIII,* Volume 1, n. 95.
[7] *Calendar of State Papers, Spain,* Supplement To Volumes 1 and 2, n. 8.
[8] Ibid., n. 7.
[9] *Calendar of State Papers, Spain,* Volume 2, 1509-1525, n. 43.
[10] *Calendar of State Papers, Spain,* Supplement To Volumes 1 and 2, n. 8.
[11] Ibid.
[12] Hall
[13] *Letters and Papers, Foreign and Domestic, Henry VIII,* Volume 1, n. 734.
[14] Ibid., n. 880.
[15] *Calendar of State Papers Relating To English Affairs in the Archives of Venice,* Volume 2, 1509-1519, n. 331.
[16] Ibid., n. 555.
[17] *Calendar of State Papers Relating To English Affairs in the Archives of Venice,* Volume 2, 1509-1519, n. 680.
[18] Ibid., n. 691.
[19] Read more about Mary and her descendants in Appendix: The Other Tudors.
[20] *Calendar of State Papers, Venice,* Volume 2, 1509-1519, n. 1103.
[21] Ibid.
[22] Jonathan Scher, Carol Dix, *Preventing Miscarriage*, p. 7.
[23] Catrina Banks Whitley and Kyra Kramer, "A New Explanation for the Reproductive Woes and Midlife Decline of Henry VIII", *The Historical Journal*, Volume 53, No. 4 (December 2010), pp. 827-848.
[24] Giles Tremlett, *Catherine of Aragon: Henry's Spanish Queen*, p. 114.
[25] *Calendar of State Papers, Spain,* Supplement To Volumes 1 and 2, n. 8.
[26] J. J. Scarisbrick, *Henry VIII*, p. 9.
[27] *Letters and Papers, Foreign and Domestic, Henry VIII,* Volume 2, n. 410.
[28] *Calendar of State Papers Relating To English Affairs in the Archives of Venice,* Volume 2, 1509-1519, n. 1230.
[29] *Calendar of State Papers Relating To English Affairs in the Archives of Venice,* Volume 4, n. 694.
[30] Catherine of Aragon, gamesiece, Museum number: A.35-1934, http://collections.vam.ac.uk/item/O96204/catherine-of-aragon-gamespiece-kels-hans
[31] The Kunsthistorisches Museum, KK 3851-77.

[32] Katherine of Aragon, attributed to Lucas Horenbout (or Hornebolte), watercolour on vellum, circa 1525-1526, NPG L244, https://www.npg.org.uk/collections/search/portrait/mw191234/Katherine-of-Aragon

[33] Catherine of Aragon, 48.1142, https://collections.mfa.org/objects/33353

Chapter 8:
"A True Maid"

On 22 June 1527, Henry VIII informed Katharine of Aragon that he wished to annul their marriage because his conscience troubled him. The King had begun to think that God was punishing him with the lack of male heirs for marrying his brother's widow. In the biblical book of Leviticus, God warned against such relationships: "Thou shalt not uncover the nakedness of thy brother's wife: it is thy brother's nakedness", and again, "If a man shall take his brother's wife, it is an impurity: he hath uncovered his brother's nakedness; they shall be childless".

By September, the Queen knew that her husband had had an affair with one of her maids of honour. Katharine was used to her husband's philandering ways, but he now wanted to marry the lady who refused to become his mistress, and to this the Queen could not agree. This lady was Anne Boleyn, daughter and niece to the Boleyn women who had served as Katharine of Aragon's ladies-in-waiting since 1509.

The King argued that he was sinfully—and thus illegally—married to Katharine of Aragon because she had carnally known his brother. Henry VIII's whole argument hinged on Katharine's first marriage being consummated and her not being a virgin when she married him in 1509. But Katharine defied Henry and intended to prove that she was not lying about the non-consummation of her marriage to Prince Arthur.

In 1529, the divorce proceedings reached the point of a public trial that took place in the Parliament chamber of the Dominican friary in London known as Blackfriars. The Queen appeared in person on 18 June 1529 with "a great company of ladies and gentlewomen following her". She threw herself on her knees and addressed Henry VIII in loud, broken English, affirming that when he first had her in his bed, she was "a true maid without touch of man; and whether it be true or no, I put it to your conscience".[1]

When papal legate Lorenzo Campeggio heard her confession, Katharine told him that she had spent only seven nights with Arthur and had emerged from this marriage "as intact and undefiled as she had come from her mother's womb".[2] The clerics and lawyers who worked to extricate Henry from his marriage agreed that "these were the worst points [against the divorce] that could be imagined".[3] These points were "the worst" because they were difficult to prove or disprove, and the only person who knew the truth was Katharine herself. Yet Henry VIII was determined to prove that his wife was a liar. Katharine may have turned her back on the proceedings at Blackfriars, but the King would proceed without her and humiliate her in the process.

Starting on 28 June 1529, a series of depositions was made concerning the witnesses to the Queen's first marriage. Amongst them were ladies-in-waiting who were now advanced in years but who in 1501 were young women. Jane Guildford, a retired lady-in-waiting in her sixties, deposed that she saw Prince Arthur and Katharine of Aragon on their wedding night "lying in bed together alone and sole and in mind and intent as she believeth to have carnal cognition together as man and wife". She left them in their bedchamber for the night and returned the next morning "as her office required" and saw them again "in bed sole, likewise as she did leave them the night before". Jane also deposed that she heard Elizabeth of York, Henry VII and Prince Arthur saying that "the said Prince Arthur and Lady Katharine lay together in bed as man and wife all alone five or six nights after the said marriage".[4]

Another lady who was with Katharine and Arthur that night was Agnes Howard, née Tilney, Dowager Duchess of Norfolk. Born in 1477, she "knew Henry VII and his Queen Elizabeth from the time she was fifteen" and remembered Katharine of Aragon's arrival from Spain. The night after their wedding, Agnes deposed, she saw Arthur and Katharine "lying in one bed . . . and left them so lying together there the said night".[5] Another lady who was present was Mary Bourchier, née Say, Countess of Essex. She was the same age as the Queen and deposed that "Prince Arthur and Katharine lived as man and wife together; that the two occupied the same bed after the wedding, at London House, and were generally reputed as man and wife".[6] This was what happened in 1501 as seen through the eyes of ladies-in-waiting who accompanied the young couple. But these depositions proved nothing and were consistent with what Katharine of Aragon herself claimed. The Queen maintained that she and Arthur slept in one bed together seven nights but never had sex.

But not only women testified during the trial. Men who served in the royal household in 1501 were called in as witnesses, and some of them were more forthcoming in their confessions. George Talbot, Earl of Shrewsbury, seneschal of the King's household, recorded that at night after the wedding, he was among the nobles who ceremonially "conducted Prince Arthur to the Lady Katharine's bedchamber, and left him there". Shrewsbury assumed that the marriage was consummated based on two factors: first, he himself was fifteen when he wedded and bedded his bride, and second, Katharine and Arthur were "always considered lawfully married during the life of Prince Arthur".[7]

Thomas Grey, Marquis of Dorset, said that he was present when Prince Arthur went to bed after his wedding and saw Katharine lying "under the coverlet, as the manner is of queens in that behalf". Dorset believed that Arthur and Katharine cohabited because the prince was "of a good and sanguine complexion, and they were commonly reputed as man and wife during Prince Arthur's life".[8]

Anthony Willoughby, who served Arthur for five years, said that he saw the prince retiring to bed with Katharine after their wedding. The next morning, Arthur emerged from his bedchamber boasting that "it is good pastime to have a wife" and calling for a cup of ale because he had been "this night in the midst of Spain".[9] The insinuation was clear: Arthur had known Katharine carnally.

Whereas the English courtiers portrayed Arthur as a boisterous youngling, the Spanish depicted him as weak and frail. In 1530, Katharine's former servants were searched for all over Spain to reply to a series of questions about Katharine's marriage to Arthur. Was it true that the marriage was not consummated because of Arthur's "extreme debility" and the fact that the act of consummation was deemed "exceedingly injurious to his health"? Was it true that "the said Arthur was very young and thin, delicate, and of a weak complexion, and unfit for a woman"? Was it "considered as a fact among the people of the royal household, Spaniards as well as Englishmen, that the said prince Arthur had not consummated his marriage" with Katharine?[10]

In 1531, at a hearing in Zaragoza, Spain, Katharine of Aragon's former attendants testified that Francesca de Caceres, who was one of Katharine's favourites, "was looking sad and telling the other ladies that nothing had passed between Prince Arthur and his wife".[11] Another witness, Dr Alcaraz, testified that Arthur's "limbs were weak and that he had never seen a man whose legs and other bits of his body were so thin".[12] To counter such rumours, Henry VIII started spreading curious reports about his late brother. Arthur, Henry claimed, had been obsessed with sex. He had strongly solicited other women for carnal copulation, showed his "erect and inflamed member" to his attendants and often complained that he was not allowed to have regular sex with Katharine.[13]

This last point rings true, as in 1501 the Spanish ambassador Fuensalida wrote that Henry VII made a decision that Arthur "will know his wife sexually on the day of the wedding and then separate himself from her for two or three years because it is said that the prince is frail, and the King . . . wanted to have them [Arthur and Katharine of Aragon] with him for the first three years [of their marriage] so that the prince should mature in strength".[14] These requirements were grounded in concern for Arthur because a surfeit of sexual activity at an early age was believed to lead to an early death.

Katharine maintained until the end of her life that she and Arthur had not consummated their short-lived marriage. She derived great satisfaction from reminding Henry that he knew perfectly well that she was a virgin when he married her. In 1529, she informed her husband that he "found her a virgin" when they married and that he often repeated that to other people at court.[15] In 1531, Katharine was even ready to swear an oath that she and

Arthur never had sex, and in 1533 the imperial ambassador Eustace Chapuys, Katharine's best friend and staunchest supporter, wrote that Henry admitted that he said to many people at court that Katharine was a virgin when they married, but the King awkwardly explained that intoxicated men say many silly things.[16]

In 1534, when a delegation from the King visited Katharine, she said: "I do greatly marvel that any wise, noble or learned men (having a conscience) will take upon them to judge or determine any such act [of consummation] to be done betwixt prince Arthur and me; and Almighty God knoweth (to whom nothing can be hid) they say untruly on me." She protested "before God that she was brought a true maid unto the King, and that neither for love of the King nor of her daughter, nor for honour or riches, would she damn her soul". She also said that there were many noblewomen about her who knew that she was a virgin "and if any of them be living I doubt not they will verify my saying".[17]

So did Katharine of Aragon and Prince Arthur know each other carnally? It may be telling that even Eustace Chapuys, Katharine's admirer and champion, thought it was "almost impossible to prove" that the marriage had not been consummated.[18] At the same time, Chapuys thought that the majority of people believed the Queen because of her godly reputation. When, in January 1536, he visited Katharine on her deathbed, Chapuys urged her to swear that what she maintained was true. He even asked the Queen's physician "to take care that she again, in extremis, declared and affirmed that she had not been known [carnally] by Prince Arthur". Yet this was never done. In a letter to Charles V, Holy Roman Emperor, Chapuys explained that "it appears that he [physician] was so much affected and troubled that he forgot it entirely".[19]

Yet it is telling that such a weighty matter was not revisited before Katharine's death. The Queen had enough time to compose a letter to Henry VIII wherein she called herself his wife and Queen. Had she, perhaps, lied the entire time about her first marriage's consummation and was afraid to meet her Maker with a falsehood on her lips? She took that knowledge to her grave.

NOTES

1 George Cavendish, *The Life of Cardinal Wolsey*, Volume 1, p. 150.
2 *Calendar of State Papers, Spain,* Volume 3 Part 2, n. 550.
3 *State Papers,* Volume 1, p. 195.
4 PRO SP 1/65, f. 19r quoted by Godfrey Anstruther, *Vaux of Harrowden: A Recusant Family*, p. 13.
5 *Letters and Papers, Foreign and Domestic, Henry VIII,* Volume 4, n. 5778.
6 Ibid.

[7] Ibid., n. 5774, 1.
[8] Ibid., n. 5774, 2.
[9] Ibid., n. 5774, 3.
[10] *Calendar of State Papers, Spain,* Volume 4 Part 1, Henry VIII, n. 572.
[11] Real Academia de Historia MS. 9-4674, quoted in Giles Tremlett, *Catherine of Aragon*, p. 89.
[12] Ibid., p. 99.
[13] H.A. Kelly, *The Matrimonial Trials of Henry VIII*, p. 153.
[14] Patrick Williams, *Katharine of Aragon*, p. 101.
[15] *Calendar of State Papers, Spain,* Volume 4 Part 1, Henry VIII, n. 224.
[16] G. W. Bernard, *The King's Reformation: Henry VIII and the Remaking of the English Church*, p. 21.
[17] *Letters and Papers, Foreign and Domestic, Henry VIII,* Volume 7, n. 786.
[18] *Calendar of State Papers, Spain,* Volume 4 Part 2, n. 641.
[19] Ibid., Volume 5 Part 2, n. 10.

CHAPTER 9: "CERTAIN DISEASES IN THE QUEEN"

It is often alleged, sometimes in historical fiction but also in scholarly works, that by 1527 Katharine of Aragon was too old to have any more children. The available evidence does not suggest that this is the case, however. While it is true that Katharine was forty-two when Henry decided to terminate their marriage, there is no evidence that she was going through menopause at the time or even before the year 1527. Henry never referred to Katharine's *inability* to bear children in general, but he always maintained that she was unable to bear him sons because she was his brother's widow, and therefore God punished them with the lack of male heirs. His main reason to repudiate Katharine and marry Anne Boleyn was his desire to produce male children. Katharine was unable to produce sons, not because she was already menopausal, but because their union was cursed and offensive to God. This was Henry's line of defence, and this he would strenuously maintain until the end of the proceedings.

Fertility was certainly not Katharine of Aragon's problem. She conceived on a regular basis, although her pregnancies resulted either in stillbirths or the early death of infants. Only Princess Mary survived the perils of early childhood and lived to reach adulthood. Katharine's last recorded pregnancy occurred in 1518, when she was thirty-three, about the same age Anne Boleyn was when she gave birth to her first child in 1533. If Henry feared she was unable to bear him any more children then, why didn't he say anything? The answer seems clear: Katharine was still deemed able to conceive.

Although the notion that Henry VIII stopped having a sexual relationship with Katharine of Aragon by 1524 is perpetuated by many historians today, primary sources tell a different story.[1] In July 1529, the issue of the Queen's first marriage's consummation was weighed in court. According to the deposition given by Thomas Boleyn, "the King and Queen cohabited till about two years ago, when he heard that the King was advised by his confessor to abstain from intercourse with the Queen, so as not to offend his conscience".[2] As the father of Henry VIII's wife-to-be, Thomas Boleyn was certainly well informed about the goings-on in the royal bedchamber.

When in late 1527 Cardinal Wolsey wrote a letter to Henry VIII's representative in Rome, he referred to "certain diseases in the Queen defying all remedy". These "diseases", Wolsey claimed, were so terrible that "the King will never live with her as a wife".[3] The implication was crystal clear: Katharine's unspeakable "diseases" were of an intimate nature. But if Katharine was indeed diseased, the same question springs to mind once again: Why didn't Henry react earlier? Perhaps because, as Katharine of Aragon's modern biographer asserts, "the Queen was not diseased", and Wolsey was desperate to obtain the annulment.[4]

In February 1528, the Venetian ambassador reported that Henry believed his marriage to Katharine was "defective and invalid" because Katharine was his brother's widow and because she was "of such an age" that he could no longer hope for offspring from her.[5] Some months later, however, Henry visited Katharine's bedchamber on several occasions and stayed overnight.[6] There is no certainty that they had resumed a sexual relationship, but it is contradictory to earlier reports about Katherine's mysterious "diseases", which allegedly led Henry to shun her bed. Henry visited Katharine's bedchamber to avoid accusations of not having sex with her: the lack of conjugal relations in a marriage was strongly condemned by religious authorities.

In 1535, when Katharine of Aragon was fifty years old, one of her staunchest supporters maintained that she was still able to bear children. The imperial ambassador Eustace Chapuys told Thomas Cromwell that should Henry VIII decide to take Katharine back as his wife, there "is every probability, as physicians and others tell me", that the King could beget male heirs from Katharine rather than "that woman", meaning Anne Boleyn. Cromwell, naturally, raised an objection; Katharine was unable to bear children "owing to her being more than forty-eight years old at this time". Chapuys, however, was well prepared and produced examples of famous Englishwomen giving birth at the age of fifty-one. Cromwell knew this was true because he had once confessed that his own mother was fifty-two when he was born.[7] This exchange throws light on Katharine of Aragon's intimate health and her ability to bear children. If she was deemed able to conceive at the age of fifty, then it means that she was not suffering from menopause at the beginning of the divorce proceedings in 1527.

NOTES

[1] See for example Robert Hutchinson, *Young Henry: The Rise of Henry VIII*, p. 134, Josephine Wilkinson, *Mary Boleyn: The True Story of Henry VIII's Favourite Mistress*, Chapter 7.

[2] *Letters and Papers, Henry VIII,* Volume 4, n. 14.

[3] Ibid., n. 3644.

[4] Giles Tremlett, *Catherine of Aragon: The Spanish Queen of Henry VIII*, p. 276.

[5] *Letters and Papers, Henry VIII,* Volume 4, n. 236.

[6] *Calendar of State Papers, Spain,* Volume 3 Part 2, n. 600.

[7] *Calendar of State Papers, Spain,* Volume 5 Part 2, n. 165.

CHAPTER 10: "DEFECTIVE CONSTITUTION"

Anne Boleyn's obstetrical history is no less complicated than that of her predecessor's. Anne herself referred to children as "the greatest consolation in this world" and bemoaned her "time and youth spent to no purpose at all" waiting for Henry VIII's divorce.[1] Her anomalous position at court—for almost seven years she was neither the King's mistress in a carnal sense nor yet his wife—meant that she had to protect herself from an unwanted pregnancy. In 1529, the perceptive French ambassador wrote that "for some time past the King has come very near Mademoiselle Anne, therefore you need not be surprised if they want to hasten it [the Blackfriars trial] because if her belly grows all will be spoilt".[2] What he was hinting at was the fact that if Anne became pregnant before the royal divorce's satisfactory accomplishment, the King would have been disparaged for being driven by lust rather than "scruple of conscience". Anne was determined to treasure her virginity, and she made it luminously clear that she would only become pregnant when married to the King. There were many people who speculated as to the true nature of Anne Boleyn's relationship with Henry VIII. Anne had certainly allowed the love-stricken King certain intimacies because his love letters are sprinkled with references to their erotic meetings. In one letter, Henry wrote that he was "wishing myself (especially an evening) in my sweetheart's arms, whose pretty dukkys [breasts] I trust shortly to kiss".[3] Some historians take it to mean that the King was referring to what he hoped would happen after the wedding, but the context of this particular letter makes it clear that he was referring to his impending meeting with Anne ("but now that I am coming towards you") which took place in November 1528 at Beddington in Surrey. The King's sexual desire underpins many of his love letters to Anne Boleyn, and this one in particular shows that Anne did not keep the King at arm's length during his quest for divorce and probably allowed a full consummation of the union to make it legally binding. In the draft of a dispensation Henry sent to the pope in 1527, he sought permission to marry a woman with whom he had already had intercourse, with whose kinswoman he had had sexual relations with in the past and who had entered into an unconsummated pre-contract with another man. This woman was undoubtedly Anne Boleyn because her sister's affair with the King required a dispensation due to the forbidden degrees of affinity, and Anne's unconsummated pre-contract with Henry Percy dating to 1523.

People speculated about Anne's virginity as ardently back then as they do now. In 1531, Simon Grynaeus, a scholar and theologian who was tasked to collect opinions about Henry VIII's divorce, wrote that although "there are those who positively deny that the King has any intercourse with her", he himself thought it unlikely. Grynaeus's verdict may have been influenced by Anne's appearance. He described her as "young, good-looking, of a rather dark complexion".[4] Just how the scholar formed the opinion that Anne was "likely enough to have children" remains unclear, but his report included speculation about her putative children. "Whether she has any children by the King I do not know", he wrote, adding that she had "not any acknowledged as such" but if she had, "they may probably be brought up in private (which, if I am not mistaken, I have heard more than once)".[5] Rumours of secret pregnancies followed in Anne's wake at the time. On 12 April 1533, the Venetian ambassador reported that "I am assured that some months ago, his Majesty espoused her, and that she bore him a son who is several months old".[6] This report was only partially true.

The summer of 1533 was a period of anticipation for Henry VIII and Anne Boleyn. On 25 January 1533, the King had married Anne against all odds, and in April of that year he had her presented to the astonished courtiers as Queen of England. By the time she was crowned on 1 June 1533, Anne was six months pregnant and made no attempt to hide it. When her father chided Anne for loosening her dress, ordering her to take away the extra panel she added to emphasise her belly "and thank God to find herself in such condition", Anne snapped back that "she was in better condition than he would have desired".[7]

Anne gloried in her pregnant state, even though when she enlarged her dress, Henry VIII was still officially married to Katharine of Aragon. Anne walked to her coronation barefoot and with her hair hanging loose down her back, heralding to the world that she was "the shining incarnation of chastity", although her belly proclaimed otherwise to the astonished crowds.[8] Having waited to start a family for so long, Anne carried her pregnant belly with pride, adding additional panels to her sophisticated gowns to accommodate her growing girth. The King was delighted and doted on Anne, showering her with luxurious items to furnish her birthing chamber. Henry gave credit to astrologers and physicians who prophesied the birth of a male heir.

Many people greeted the unfolding events with silent astonishment at Anne's elevation in rank, but only one man had the audacity to point out that a new marriage was not automatically a promise of sons. Eustace Chapuys, the imperial ambassador and a tireless champion of Katharine of Aragon, told the King that his seventeen-year-old daughter Mary was not only "endowed with all imaginable goodness and virtue" but also "of an age to bear children". She, Chapuys postulated, could be the means of prolonging the Tudor dynasty. To back up his point, Chapuys said that Henry VIII himself had attained the crown through a female line so "nature seemed to oblige him to restore it to the Princess". Henry VIII was growing irritated with each word coming out of the ambassador's mouth. "He replied that he knew better than his daughter", Chapuys later reported, "and that he wished to have children". The King was forty-two years old, and his best years were behind him, or so everybody thought. Everybody except Henry himself. Anne Boleyn inspired him to seek annulment; she promised him male heirs, and she would be the means to provide them. Chapuys seemed to read the King's mind when he said that he could not be sure of having more children. "You are not privy to all my secrets", Henry roared in anger. "Am I not a man like others?" he asked three times in a row. Chapuys made his own conclusions. The King was implying that his "beloved lady"—or the "Concubine", as Chapuys often referred to her in his despatches—was pregnant.[9] This exchange proves just how much depended on the outcome of Anne Boleyn's pregnancy. Henry VIII once warned her that he "was offending everyone and making enemies everywhere for her sake".[10] Now he desired to prove to the world that he had been right all along. If Anne gave birth to a son, every decision would have been justified. The King would have had an heir. And then another. Or so he hoped.

Anne Boleyn entered her confinement chamber on 26 August 1533. Rumours on the Continent had it that she gave birth to a monster or that her child was stillborn.[11] These rumours stemmed from the fact that many people in Catholic Europe believed that Henry VIII's marriage to Anne was unlawful because he already had a wife when he married Anne. Henry VIII was so convinced that Anne would give him a son that he picked a name in advance of the birth—he hesitated between Edward and Henry—and started making preparations for a festive tournament. Also, the courtly astrologers and physicians assured him that Anne was pregnant with a boy.

Yet on 7 September 1533, Anne Boleyn gave birth to a baby girl who was named Elizabeth, after both of her grandmothers. The lavish tournaments and feasts were cancelled and an extra letter *S* had to be added to the word "prince" announcing the birth of a long-awaited male heir. The imperial ambassador made much of the fact that Henry VIII's first child by Anne Boleyn was not a son but a daughter and asserted that both were disheartened. Yet whatever their private feelings, Henry and Anne arranged a splendid christening and demanded that their daughter was accepted as an heiress to the throne.

On 28 January 1534, Chapuys reported that Anne was "pregnant and in condition to have more children".[12] In April, a courtier reported from Greenwich Palace that the Queen "hath a goodly belly, praying our Lord to send us a prince".[13] That month Henry and Anne visited their daughter, Elizabeth, at Eltham Palace, which had served as a royal nursery since the reign of Edward IV. At Eltham, the royal couple made necessary arrangements "against the coming of the Prince".[14] These preparations included the setting of the iron canopy over the richly decorated cradle, special measures to exclude draughts and the repainting of the prince's chamber with yellow ochre. In the beginning of July 1534, the King sent Anne's brother, George Boleyn, as an ambassador to the French court to postpone the intended trip to Calais. The ambassador was to tell the French King's sister that it was Anne who wished to defer the interview because she was unable to leave England on account of her advanced pregnancy and desired to have Henry at her side when her child was born.

How this pregnancy ended remains one of the unsolved mysteries of Anne Boleyn's life. There is no hint of evidence that Anne withdrew from public life to enter her confinement chamber, as it was reported in August 1533 before the birth of Elizabeth. The Queen was last seen with a "fair belly" on 24 June 1534, and two days later she and Henry VIII were reportedly "merry" at Hampton Court.[15] At this point, Anne disappears from the record.

On 2 July 1534, Henry VIII summoned Thomas Howard, Duke of Norfolk, and Thomas Cromwell, his secretary, to meet him at the More. It was at the More that the King sent George Boleyn to France with instructions to defer the interview with Francis I in Calais, citing Anne's advanced pregnancy as an excuse. It is highly likely that Anne's pregnancy ended before 2 July 1534 because this would explain the King's reluctance to meet face-to-face with Francis I, who was the father of three healthy sons. Certainly, Henry knew very well that Anne was pregnant before he cancelled the meeting, and the available evidence suggests that he intended it to be an all-male assembly.

In a conversation with her brother in June 1534, Anne told him that when the King went to Calais for the meeting and she would be made regent ("as she will be", reported the imperial ambassador, based on what he heard at court), she would not hesitate to harm Henry's daughter Mary.[16] This suggests that Henry VIII intended to leave Anne behind as regent in England all along. In this light, his decision to cancel the summit in Calais made no sense at all unless he was trying to avoid it at all costs.

Anne Boleyn did not accompany Henry VIII on his annual royal progress in the summer. On 18 July 1534, a courtier named John Husee reported that the King reached Woking in Surrey, from whence he departed to Eltham Palace (perhaps to visit his daughter Elizabeth) and then "he will meet with the Queen at Guildford".[17] By Henry VIII's reign, Guildford Castle was not a royal residence, but it served as one of many stops during summer progresses. It is not clear when Anne reached Guildford. She appears to have given birth to a stillborn child of unknown sex at

Hampton Court between 26 June and 2 July 1534. She arrived at Guildford Castle between 2 and 18 July 1534 to recover after this traumatic experience. The King reached Guildford on 28 July and stayed there until 7 August. It remains unknown whether Anne accompanied her husband when he left. On 27 September 1534, the imperial ambassador picked up a rumour that Henry VIII "began to doubt whether his lady was enceinte [pregnant] or not".[18] Chapuys's brief note led medical historian Sir John Dewhurst to form a theory that she suffered from phantom pregnancy (pseudocyesis):

"This curious disorder, which is associated with visible swelling of the abdomen despite the fact that no pregnancy exists, classically occurs in women who are desperate to prove their fertility or who dread the possibility that an unguarded act of intercourse might have led to an unwanted conception. Anne was certainly in the former category, since her very life, literally, depended upon giving the King the son he longed for."[19]

Dewhurst and historians who subscribe to his theory postulate that if Anne were indeed pregnant, the King would have no reason to "doubt" whether she was with child. Yet Anne's biographer Eric Ives argued that the

Queen did not suffer from phantom pregnancy because she "had no reason to be under stress at this date, having produced a healthy female child eight months earlier".[20] She seems to have conceived almost immediately after the birth of Elizabeth, possibly in November 1533, only a month after the churching ceremony.

There exists one curious piece of country gossip suggesting that Anne Boleyn lost her child through a premature birth. In February 1535, some seven months after the harrowing events of 1534, a woman by the name Margaret Chancellor from the county of Suffolk was forced to confess before a royal administrative that, when drunk and under the influence of an evil spirit, she had said, in the presence of witnesses, that "the Queen's Grace had one child by our Sovereign Lord the King, which the said child was dead born, and she prayed she might never have other".[21] These words certainly referred to the outcome of Anne Boleyn's 1534 pregnancy.

Rumours were often just that, false tales, but this one is way too specific to ignore it. It's timing—seven months after Anne's pregnancy ended in mysterious circumstances—lends it credibility. What's more, the sole fact that Margaret Chancellor was interrogated points to the possibility that the King's authorities were eager to supress such tales, regardless of whether they were true or false, because they could have been used to say that Henry VIII's marriage to Anne Boleyn did not have God's divine approval.

There is also one more aspect of this pregnancy. Historians often refer to it as a miscarriage, but the discussed evidence points out that Anne Boleyn was in her seventh month of pregnancy when the premature birth occurred, so it was a stillbirth. She was pregnant from 23 January 1534 (Chapuys's comment) to either 26 June (when she was seen in a jovial mood with the King at Hampton Court) or 2 July (when Henry VIII cancelled his meeting with Francis I because of Anne's advanced pregnancy). By definition, miscarriage is losing a baby during the first twenty weeks of pregnancy.[22] The twentieth week of pregnancy is about the fifth month, and the evidence points out that Anne was approximately in her seventh month, so she did not miscarry but gave birth to a stillborn child. The baby's sex remains unknown.

Some historians state that Anne Boleyn was pregnant in June 1535, but this stems from the misdated letter of Sir William Kingston to Lord Lisle wherein Kingston mentions Anne's "fair belly".[23] In the same letter,

Kingston sends greetings to "Master Porter" and his wife. Muriel St Clare Byrne, editor of *The Lisle Letters*, pointed out that this reference makes it clear that "this letter must belong to 1533 or 1534, and not to 1535 as dated by *Letters and Papers*", because the married Master Porter was Sir Christopher Garneys, who died in October 1534, and he was succeeded by an unmarried Sir Thomas Palmer.

Whereas it's clear that Anne Boleyn was not visibly pregnant in the summer of 1535, she conceived later that year. In *The Royal Progress and Anne Boleyn's Visit to Winchester in 1535*, Dr Brian M. Collins suggested that "if we assume that medieval women counted their pregnancy to have started from the day they missed their menstruation, then to calculate the date of conception, two weeks should be added to the fifteen weeks stated by Anne when she miscarried on 29 January 1536. Thus conception would have occurred in a two week period either side of 2 October 1535".[24] Conception at about this date makes it understandable why Anne ordered "a book of physick [medicine]" in late October 1535.[25]

Unfortunately, this pregnancy also ended in personal tragedy when the Queen miscarried on 29 January 1536, the day of Katharine of Aragon's funeral. Charles Wriothesley, the Windsor herald, recorded that the Queen "had reckoned herself at that time but fifteen weeks gone with child".[26] Anne herself ascribed the loss of her child to two factors. First, when she learned that her husband had fallen from his horse during a celebratory joust held at Greenwich Palace to celebrate Katharine of Aragon's death, she panicked. It was because her uncle, the Duke of Norfolk, burst into her chamber and informed her of the King's fall in the most unnerving manner. Second, when the King visited her shortly after her miscarriage, she told him it nearly broke her heart "when she saw that he loved others", referring to Henry's recent affair with one of Anne's maids of honour, Jane Seymour.[27] Later sources claimed that Anne caught Jane sitting on Henry VIII's lap and exclaimed: "I saw this harlot Jane sitting on your knees while my belly was doing its duty!"[28] There might be an element of truth in this story, as it also appears in the works of Catholic writers who were usually hostile towards Anne. In the memoir of Jane Dormer, Duchess of Feria, we find the following scene:

"The King seeming to affect Jane Seymour, and having her on his knee, as Queen Anne espied, who then was thought to be with child, she for anger and disdain miscarried, as she said, betwitting the King with it, who willed her to pardon him, and he would not displease her in that kind thereafter."[29]

According to Nicholas Sander, a Catholic priest who was writing in the 1580s, in 1536 Anne gave birth to a "shapeless mass of flesh".[30] This prompted modern historian Retha M. Warnicke to hypothesise that Anne gave birth to a deformed foetus and that the King took it as a sign their marriage was doomed.[31] Yet the phrase used by Sander was not unusual in terms of sixteenth-century terminology for miscarriage. For example, when Margaret of Austria miscarried her child in 1497, one chronicler noted: "Instead of the desired offspring, she has aborted; instead of the longed for heir, we have been given an unformed mass of flesh worthy of pity."[32] There was no suggestion that Margaret's child was deformed. Rather, the unformed or shapeless "mass of flesh" in both cases indicated that the pregnancy was in its early stages.

Not everyone, however, believed that the Queen had miscarried. The hostile imperial correspondent at the French court reported, with a streak of malicious glee, that "that woman pretended to have miscarried of a son, not being really with child, and, to keep up the deceit, would allow no one to attend on her but her sister".[33] Just why Anne would end her allegedly pretended pregnancy in the fifteenth week remains unclear, and the report contains a reference to Anne's sister, who was banished from court in

1534. The better-informed imperial ambassador Chapuys concluded that "the general opinion is that the Concubine's miscarriage was entirely owing to defective constitution and her utter inability to bear male children".[34] Was Anne's constitution truly "defective"? What do we really know about the state of her health?

In general, it appears that Anne Boleyn enjoyed good health. In May 1528, she was separated from Katharine of Aragon's ladies-in-waiting, who suffered from an outbreak of smallpox, and placed in her own chamber in Tiltyard Towers at Greenwich Palace.[35] On 6 June that same year, a courtier close to her observed that "Mistress Anne is very well amended", suggesting that she recovered her health after some ailment, perhaps the dreaded smallpox.[36] On 18 June 1528, the French ambassador Cardinal Jean du Bellay reported that two days earlier one of Anne Boleyn's maids of honour fell ill with the sweating sickness.

According to some hostile sources, Anne had some congenital abnormalities. Writing during the 1580s, Nicholas Sander stated that:

"Anne Boleyn was rather tall of stature, with black hair, and an oval face of a sallow complexion, as if troubled with jaundice. She had a projecting tooth under the upper lip, and on her right hand six fingers. There was a large wen under her chin, and therefore to hide its ugliness she wore a high dress covering her throat. In this, she was followed by the ladies of the court, who also wore high dresses, having before been in the habit of leaving their necks and the upper portion of their persons uncovered. She was handsome to look at, with a pretty mouth, amusing in her ways, playing well on the lute, and was a good dancer."[37]

Those who knew her asserted that she did not have a sixth finger on her right hand but rather a barely visible "little show of a nail" on one of her fingers. She also had "certain small moles" on her body.[38] Recent research proves that a "large wen" she supposedly had under her chin stems from the error of the nineteenth-century translator because in the original Latin text Sander suggested that Anne had a swelling under her chin, but he was not sure what it was, and he did not use the word "large" in describing it.[39] There is, however, a justification of the translator's "large" wen. An anonymous observer of imperial affiliations who was present at Anne's coronation in 1533 wrote that:

"The crown became her very ill, and a wart disfigured her very much. She wore a violet velvet mantle, with a high ruff of gold thread and pearls, which concealed a swelling she has, resembling goitre."[40]

Historians usually dismiss this report as hostile, citing the fact that high ruffs were not yet fashionable in Henry VIII's day. Yet there is a ring of truth to this description because, as costume historian Maria Hayward pointed out in her book, Anne certainly owned a spectacular "partlet containing a collar" which formed part of the Queen's collection of jewels; it was heavily embellished with gold, various pearls, diamonds, rubies and emeralds.[41] Partlets covered shoulders and often the wearer's neck as well. Anne had also exchanged the heavy crown for a lighter one to ease her head and not because it did not fit her—it's another hint that the hostile report was at least partially truthful. It is therefore reasonable to assume that Anne had some sort of a swelling under her chin. Hans Holbein's sketch with the inscription "Anna Bollein Queen" confirms this.

Shortly before her death in May 1536, the imperial ambassador, with his typical sarcasm and penchant for wordplay, compared Anne to a "thin, old and vicious hack", suggesting that she grew thin at the end of her marriage, perhaps as a result of stress.[42] In her controversial piece entitled *Royal Bodies*, historical novelist Hilary Mantel suggested that "If this is true, and we put it together with reports of a swelling in her throat, and with the description of her by one contemporary as 'a goggle-eyed whore', then we're looking, possibly, at a woman with a hyperthyroid condition, a woman of frayed temper who lives on the end of her nerves".[43] This is a fascinating theory, but with the lack of solid supportive evidence it remains only a tantalising possibility. The truth about Anne Boleyn's health is that she was generally of good health—she managed to survive the dreaded sweating sickness, and there are hardly any references to her ill health other than those from 1528—and there is no reason to assume that she was sickly. Her inability to produce a male heir may have had more to do with Henry VIII's health than with her own, as will be seen in chapter 12.

NOTES

[1] *Calendar of State Papers, Spain,* Volume 4 Part 1, n. 224.
[2] *Letters and Papers, Foreign and Domestic, Henry VIII,* Volume 4, n. 5679.
[3] Elizabeth Norton, *Anne Boleyn: Henry VIII's Obsession*, p. 23.
[4] Philip W. Sergeant, *The Life of Anne Boleyn*, p. 180.
[5] Ibid.
[6] *Calendar of State Papers Relating to English Affairs in the Archives of Venice,* Volume 4, n. 870.
[7] *Letters and Papers, Foreign and Domestic, Henry VIII,* Volume 6, n. 556.
[8] Eric Ives, *The Life and Death of Anne Boleyn*, p. 225.
[9] *Calendar of State Papers, Spain,* Volume 4 Part 2, n. 1061.
[10] Ibid., Volume 4 Part 1, n. 373.
[11] *Letters and Papers, Foreign and Domestic, Henry VIII,* Volume 6, n. 1065.
[12] *Letters and Papers, Foreign and Domestic, Henry VIII,* , Volume 7, n. 114.

---

[13] Ibid., n. 56.
[14] Eric Ives, *The Life and Death of Anne Boleyn*, p. 249.
[15] *Letters and Papers, Foreign and Domestic, Henry VIII*, Volume 7, n. 888. See also Muriel St Clare Byrne, *The Lisle Letters*, Volume 1, p. 477.
[16] *Letters and Papers, Foreign and Domestic, Henry VIII*, Volume 7, n. 871.
[17] Ibid., n. 989.
[18] Ibid., n. 1193.
[19] Sir John Dewhurst, *The Alleged Miscarriages of Catherine of Aragon and Anne Boleyn*, p. 55.
[20] Eric Ives, *The Life and Death of Anne Boleyn*, p. 394.
[21] Roger B. Merriman, *Life and Letters of Thomas Cromwell*, Volume 1, p. 117.
[22] Jonathan Scher, Carol Dix, *Preventing Miscarriage*, p. 7.
[23] Muriel St Clare Byrne, *The Lisle Letters*, Volume 1, p. 477.
[24] Brian M. Collins, *The Royal Progress and Anne Boleyn's Visit to Winchester in 1535*, p. 12.
[25] *Letters and Papers, Foreign and Domestic, Henry VIII*, Volume 9, n. 723.
[26] Charles Wriothesley, *A Chronicle of England During the Reigns of the Tudors*, Volume 1, p. 33.
[27] *Letters and Papers, Foreign and Domestic, Henry VIII*, Volume 10, n. 351.
[28] Eric Ives, *The Life and Death of Anne Boleyn*, p. 304.
[29] Henry Clifford, *The Life of Jane Dormer, Duchess of Feria*, p. 79.
[30] Nicolas Sander, *The Rise and Growth of the Anglican Schism*, p. 132.
[31] Retha M. Warnicke, *The Rise and Fall of Anne Boleyn*, Cambridge University Press, 1991.
[32] Peggy K. Liss, *Isabel the Queen: Life and Times*, p. 367.
[33] *Letters and Papers, Foreign and Domestic, Henry VIII*, Volume 10, n. 450.
[34] *Calendar of State Papers, Spain*, Volume 5 Part 2, n. 21.
[35] *Letters and Papers, Foreign and Domestic, Henry VIII*, Volume 4, Introduction.
[36] Ibid., n. 4335.
[37] Nicolas Sander, *The Rise and Growth of the Anglican Schism*, p. 25.
[38] George Cavendish, *The Life and Death of Cardinal Wolsey*, p. 430.
[39] Sylwia S. Zupanec, *The Daring Truth About Anne Boleyn*, p. 14.
[40] *Letters and Papers, Foreign and Domestic, Henry VIII*, Volume 6, n. 585.

---

[41] Maria Hayward, *Dress at the Court of King Henry VIII*, p. 167.
[42] *Calendar of State Papers, Spain,* Volume 5 Part 2, n. 55.
[43] Hilary Mantel, "Royal Bodies", *London Review of Books*, Volume 35 No 4, pp. 3-7. [http://www.lrb.co.uk/v35/n04/hilary-mantel/royal-bodies]

Chapter 11: "Suspicions of poison"

Katharine of Aragon died on 7 January 1536 at the age of fifty-one. Henry VIII was ecstatic, exclaiming, "God be praised that we are free from all suspicion of war".[1] Katharine's death removed a political threat since Charles V would not invade England to restore his aunt to her proper place now that she was dead. Still, the manner of Katharine's death seemed suspicious to many, chief among them the imperial ambassador Eustace Chapuys.

Katharine's illness started in early December 1535. Chapuys learned about it from Thomas Cromwell, who said that the former Queen was "very sick". Katharine's chief physician, the Spanish Dr Miguel de la Sa informed Chapuys that "with God's help, her illness would be nothing at all". On 13 December, Chapuys wrote to Charles V that "thank God, she has recovered, and is now well."[2] Unfortunately, on 25 December Katharine had a remission of her illness. "The symptoms were pains in the stomach, so violent and acute that she could not retain the smallest particle of food or drink", Chapuys related to Charles V.[3] Knowing that for the past five years Anne Boleyn often boasted that she would use poison to get rid of her rival, the imperial ambassador started entertaining doubts as to whether Katharine's illness was natural: "I have many a time asked the physician who attended her, whether he had any suspicions of poison having been administered." Miguel de la Sa wasn't sure but suspected that poison was certainly a possibility:

"His answer has always been that he had some doubts about it, for that since she had drunk of beer brought from Wales, she had never felt well. The poison, if there was any, must have been very subtle and refined, for he had been unable to discover externally any traces of it in her body, such as pure and simple poison would inevitably leave. Should she be embalmed, he added, we shall know for certain."[4]

Knowing that Katherine's life was in danger, Chapuys applied to the King for permission to see her. Permission granted, the imperial ambassador mounted his horse "in order to repair in all possible haste to the Queen's residence, followed by a numerous suite of my own servants and friends". He reached Kimbolton Castle on 2 January 1536. Katharine was happy to see Eustace, thanked him "for the many services" he had rendered to her over the years and said she was happy to see him "at a time too when, if it should please God to take her to Himself, it would at least be a consolation to die as it were in his arms, and not all alone like a beast".[5]

Chapuys's visit lifted Katharine's spirits. He stayed with her for four days, having several long audiences, and it appeared that Katharine would rally:

> "After four days spent in the above manner, perceiving that the Queen began little by little to recover her sleep and to get rest—that her stomach retained food, and that she was evidently getting much better—she herself was of opinion, as well as her physician, who now considered her out of danger, that I ought at once to return home, not only in order not to abuse the permission granted to me by the King, but also to ask for a better residence for her, as promised at my departure from London. I took, therefore, leave of the Queen on Tuesday evening; she being then, to all appearance, happy and contented, so much so that on the very evening of my departure I saw her smile two or three times, and half an hour after I had left she would still joke with one of my suite, rather inclined to a jest, who had casually remained behind."[6]

On Wednesday, 5 January, Chapuys was informed that Katharine "slept well, and her physician gave full hope of her recovery; so much so that he advised me to return to London immediately, adding that should there be a relapse or danger of life he would not fail to let me know". Knowing this, Chapuys packed his belongings and ordered his suite to go with him to London. He rode "as leisurely as possible to wait for news, though I must say none came to me on the road".[7]

It was in London that Chapuys received "the very grievous, painful, and lamentable news" of Katharine of Aragon's death, which "occurred on Friday, the day after the Epiphany, towards two o'clock in the afternoon".[8] Eighth hours after her death, Henry VIII ordered a postmortem autopsy to discern the cause of Katharine's death. Chapuys was outraged that none of the members of Katharine's household were present, writing:

"[N]o one was allowed to be present, not even her confessor or physician, but only the candle-maker of the house and one servant and a companion of the one who opened her, and although it was not their business, and they were no surgeons, yet they have often done such a duty."[9]

Here, Chapuys demonstrated that after seven years at the Tudor court he still sometimes had problems with

English customs. The "candle-maker" who performed the postmortem was no ordinary candle-maker but a member of the Wax Chandlers' Company. Their business originally included the making of torches, tapers and candles, but they were also called in for embalming because the wax chandlers were a minor medical guild. Katharine was embalmed and cered by the wax chandler, laid in lead by the plumber and, thus prepared, would await her burial.

According to Chapuys, the wax chandler informed Katharine's confessor, Bishop of Llandalf, "in great secrecy and as if his life depended on it":

"[T]hat he had found the Queen's body and the intestines perfectly sound and healthy, as if nothing had happened, with the single exception of the heart, which was completely black, and of a most hideous aspect; after washing it in three different waters, and finding that it did not change colour, he cut it in two, and found that it was the same inside, so much so that after being washed several times it never changed colour.

"The man also said that he found inside the heart something black and round, which adhered strongly to the concavities. And moreover, after this spontaneous declaration on the part of the man, my secretary having asked the Queen's physician whether he thought the Queen had died of poison, the latter answered that in his opinion there was no doubt about it, for the bishop [of Llandaff] had been told so under confession, and besides that, had not the secret been revealed, the symptoms, the course, and the fatal end of her illness were a proof of that."[10]

Chapuys firmly believed that Katharine of Aragon was poisoned, and he made it clear in his despatches that he blamed the King and Anne Boleyn. Following Katharine's death, Chapuys wrote that many at court believed she was poisoned and that the poison "came from Italy".[11] In a letter to Nicholas Perrenot, seigneur de Granvelle, Chapuys elaborated more, writing that it was rumoured the poison came from Henry VIII's ambassador in Rome, Gregorio di Casale, via his English agent Gurone Bertano.[12] Writing from the imperial court on 30 January 1536, the English ambassador Philip Hoby wrote that "there is great talk here that my lady Dowager is dead, and that she was poisoned by the King's procurement".[13] Rumours of foul play were rife. Three years later Duchess Christina of Milan abhorred the offer of becoming Henry VIII's fourth wife, saying that she suspected that Katharine, her great aunt, had been poisoned.[14]

Henry VIII never publicised the outcome of Katharine's autopsy, so perhaps he too believed that his former wife's death was hastened. Considering how fast and with what ease he proceeded against Anne Boleyn, he may have believed Anne had something to do with Katharine's death. During Anne's trial for treason on 15 May 1536, Chapuys mentioned that among the charges lodged against Anne was that "she had poisoned the late Queen, and meditated doing the same with the Princess [Lady Mary]".[15] Dr Pedro Ortiz, Katharine of Aragon's former proctor in Rome, wrote to Empress Isabella that certain "persons in England, to whom we have written to inquire into this most strange event [Anne's execution], assert that during the inquiry instituted to prove Anne's guilt, it was found that she had tried to poison Her Highness, Queen Katharine of England".[16]

If Chapuys is to be believed, when Anne was arrested, Henry VIII told his illegitimate son, FitzRoy, that he and Mary were lucky to have "escaped the hands of that accursed whore, who had determined to poison them".[17] When FitzRoy died two months after Anne's execution, rumours abounded that Anne and her brother had administered a slow-working poison.[18] Despite all of these rumours, it's unlikely that Anne really poisoned Katharine.

She had a loose tongue and often boasted that she would use poison to get rid of Katharine and Mary, but if she truly wanted to get rid of Katharine, it made much more sense to do it during the long years of prolonged divorce proceedings rather than later.

But if Katharine wasn't poisoned, what was the cause of her death? Her final illness lasted from the beginning of December 1535 to 7 January 1536, and she had brief intervals in between, giving good hope of recovery. Medical scientist Sir Arthur MacNalty proposed that Katharine died of secondary melanotic sarcoma, a form of cancer.[19] Historians today widely agree with this diagnosis.[20]

Eustace Chapuys reported Katharine's last hours with great detail. In the evening of 6 January, the Feast of Epiphany, she felt so well that she combed and tied her hair without assistance. On 7 January, "an hour after midnight", she began to ask what time it was, "and if it was near day". She wanted to hear Mass and receive the sacrament. Chapuys continued:

"When day broke she heard Mass and received the sacrament with the utmost fervour, and thereafter continued to repeat some beautiful orisons, and begged the bystanders to pray for her soul, and that God would pardon the King her husband the wrong he had done her, and that the divine goodness would lead him to the true road and give him good counsel. Afterwards she received extreme unction, applying herself to the whole office very devoutly."[21]

It was in this state of mind that Katharine decided to write one last letter to Henry VIII, addressing him as her "most dear lord, king and husband":

"The hour of my death now drawing on, the tender love I owe you forced me, my case being such, to commend myself to you, and to put you in remembrance with a few words of the health and safeguard of your soul which you ought to prefer before all worldly matters, and before the care and pampering of your body, for the which you have cast me into many calamities and yourself into many troubles. For my part, I pardon you everything, and I wish to devoutly pray God that He will pardon you also. For the rest, I commend unto you our daughter Mary, beseeching you to be a good father unto her, as I have heretofore desired. I entreat you also, on behalf of my maids, to give them marriage portions, which is not much, they being but three. For all my other servants I solicit the wages due them, and a year more, lest they be unprovided for. Lastly, I make this vow, that mine eyes desire you above all things.

Katharine the Queen."[22]

English law forbade a wife from making a last will during her husband's life, and so Katharine ordered her physician to write a short list of requests to be submitted to Henry VIII in lieu of a will. She signed them and handed them to the only man she knew would honour her last wishes: Eustace Chapuys.

One of Katharine's recent biographers believes that the letter is a product of later Catholic propaganda and is, therefore, "almost certainly fictitious".[23] However, the letter written by Katharine shortly before her death is mentioned in a contemporary source describing her funeral procession. The anonymous author was disgusted that rumours alleging "that in the hour of death, she acknowledged she had not been Queen of England" were spread in England shortly after Katharine's demise. He knew that it was not true "because at that hour, she ordered a writing to be made in her name addressed to the King as her husband, and to the ambassador of the Emperor, her nephew, which she signed with these words: Katharine, Queen of England, commending her ladies and servants to the favour of the said ambassador".[24] This account tallies with what we know about Katharine of Aragon's letter—she had indeed addressed it to "my lord and dear husband"—and signed a request to Henry entreating him to be good to her servants.

One of the most persistent myths about Katharine of Aragon's last hours is that she died in the arms of her Spanish lady-in-waiting and friend Maria de Salinas, Lady Willoughby.[25] Maria "who has faithfully served her [Katharine of Aragon], and who has always comforted her in her hours of trial", had received letters patent of denization and married William Willoughby, Baron Willoughby de Eresby, in 1516.[26] Katharine of Aragon and Henry VIII had financed Lady Willoughby's marriage, giving her a dowry worth eleven hundred marks. She was so much favoured by Katharine that it was said that the Queen loved her "more than any other mortal".[27] In July 1534, Maria, whose only daughter married Charles Brandon, Duke of Suffolk, was forced to leave Katharine's service. Distressed, Chapuys recorded this fact, writing that "even a Spanish lady who has remained with her all her life, and has served her at her own expense, is forbidden to see her".[28]

"I heard say that my mistress is very sore sick again", Maria wrote in a letter to Secretary Thomas Cromwell on 30 December 1535. She desired to see Katharine, but she needed a special licence from the King. "I pray you remember me of your goodness", she urged Cromwell, "for you did promise me to labour the King's Grace to get me licence to go to her Grace afore God send for her; for, as I am informed, there is no other likelihood but it shall be shortly".[29] Maria feared that she would be unable to see Katharine for the last time, but Cromwell was unmoved and failed to reply.

Maria decided to defy both Thomas Cromwell and Henry VIII, and on 1 January 1536, she travelled on horseback through snowy weather to the remote Kimbolton Castle, Katharine of Aragon's residence. She reached her destination at six o'clock in the afternoon and knocked at the castle's doors. Katharine of Aragon's servants were dismayed to see Maria, whom they did not expect. Maria claimed she had a fall from her horse while travelling. She was distressed and, in a bid for sympathy, told Katharine's chamberlain that "she thought never to have seen the Princess Dowager again by reason of such tidings as she had heard of her". But the chamberlain demanded to see the licence, which Maria did not have. "It was ready to be showed", she replied, but when she left Kimbolton after seeing Katharine for the last time, the chamberlain wrote on 5 January that "since that time we never saw her" nor "any letters of her licence hither to repair".[30]

NOTES

[1] *Letters and Papers, Foreign and Domestic, Henry VIII,* Volume 10, n. 141.
[2] Ibid., Volume 9, n. 964.
[3] *Calendar of State Papers, Spain,* Volume 5 Part 2, n. 3.
[4] Ibid.
[5] Ibid.
[6] Ibid.
[7] Ibid.
[8] Ibid.
[9] *Letters and Papers, Foreign and Domestic, Henry VIII,* Volume 10, n. 141.
[10] *Calendar of State Papers, Spain,* Volume 5 Part 2, n. 9.
[11] Ibid., n. 10.
[12] *Letters and Papers, Foreign and Domestic, Henry VIII,* Volume 10, n. 200.
[13] Ibid., n. 208.
[14] Ibid., Volume 14 Part 2, n. 400.
[15] *Calendar of State Papers, Spain,* Volume 5 Part 2, n. 55.
[16] Ibid., n. 58.
[17] *Letters and Papers, Foreign and Domestic, Henry VIII,* Volume 10, n. 908.
[18] Read more in Chapter 13.
[19] Sir Arthur S. MacNalty, "The Death of Queen Catherine of Aragon", *Nursing Mirror,* 28 December 1962.
[20] See for example Giles Tremlett, *Catherine of Aragon*, p. 424, J. J. Scarisbrick, *Henry VIII*, p. 334.
[21] *Letters and Papers, Foreign and Domestic, Henry VIII,* Volume 10, n. 141.
[22] Patrick Williams, *Katharine of Aragon*, p. 374.

---

[23] Giles Tremlett, *Catherine of Aragon*, p. 422.

[24] *Letters and Papers, Foreign and Domestic*, Volume 10, note 284.

[25] I found that the earliest reference to this myth comes from the 1962 biography *Catherine, Duchess of Suffolk: A Portrait* by Evelyn Read. It was repeated in subsequent biographies including the 1970 *A Crown for Elizabeth* by Mary M. Luke, 1977 *Women of Action in Tudor England* by Pearl Hogrefe and 1996 *The Six Wives of Henry VIII* by Antonia Fraser.

[26] *Calendar of State Papers, Spain,* Volume 2, n. 238.

[27] Ibid., n. 201.

[28] *Letters and Papers, Foreign and Domestic, Henry VIII,* Volume 7, n. 1013.

[29] M.A. Everett Wood, *Letters of Royal and Illustrious Ladies of Great Britain,* Volume 2, pp. 208-9.

[30] *Letters and Papers, Foreign and Domestic, Henry VIII,* Volume 10, n. 28.

CHAPTER 12: "NEITHER SKILL NOR VIRILITY"

The loss of a child in January 1536 shocked Anne, who, according to the imperial ambassador, frequently wept because she feared she would end up like the late Katharine of Aragon. But she remained hopeful, telling her ladies-in-waiting who comforted her after the loss that "it was for the best, because she would be the sooner with child again, and that the son she bore would not be doubtful like this one, which had been conceived during the life of the Queen [Katharine]".[1] There was no reason why Anne would not have a son. Both of her grandmothers had produced a large brood of children including several boys. Her mother had three, although two of them died in childhood. Her sister, Mary, the King's former mistress, had one precious son who may have been Henry's bastard. Now it was Anne's turn.

Her "apparent aptness to procreation of children", measured by the childbearing potential of her closest female relatives, was her asset.[2] Indeed, it was her best quality in the King's eyes during their courtship. Yet she failed. Her first pregnancy resulted in the birth of Elizabeth, the future Queen Elizabeth I, and two more ended in tragedies. Henry was tired of waiting and tired of Anne. He expected a male heir and an unconditional obedience. Anne, who played the part of a seductive royal mistress for years, failed spectacularly at both tasks. She found it difficult, if not impossible, to conform to her husband's distorted idea of marriage. Were they not partners and equals during the years of their courtship? Why now must she be perceived merely as a broodmare? She had more than that to offer. But to fail at childbearing was to fail as a queen and as a wife. The lack of a son defined her as literally barren since the King compared having daughters to being childless. In Henry VIII's view, Anne Boleyn was old news. She had to go.

Anne was not exactly blindly in love with Henry either. In the privacy of her apartments, she laughed at her husband. She and her brother mocked the King's poetry and fashion sense, and George in particular made some bawdy jokes regarding his niece's paternity. Anne also told her sister-in-law that Henry VIII had "neither the skill nor virility" as a lover, and it was reported that she could "never love the King in her heart" and appeared tired of married life with him.[3] These may have been "little follies", but to the King they amounted to "great crimes" because they questioned his manhood and talents.[4] Jokes with sexual innuendos appear to have been commonplace within Anne's private space. During her imprisonment, as she learned that not only her brother but also poet Thomas Wyatt were arrested, she quipped that if they could not make their pallets (beds) properly, they might at least be able to make ballets (ballads), referring to their ability to write poetry. One of the women who attended Anne admonished her, saying that "such desire as you have had to such tales have brought you to this".[5]

On 2 May 1536, Anne was arrested and taken by barge to the Tower of London. Accused of adultery, incest and treasonous plotting to kill the King, she was amazed and could hardly believe what was happening. When the Tower gate closed behind her and the councillors who escorted her left, she broke down in tears. "Master Kingston, shall I go into a dungeon?" William Kingston, her gaoler, replied that royal apartments wherein she was lodged during her coronation festivities were prepared for her. "It is too good for me", she sobbed hysterically.

At first, Anne was kept in the dark as to the exact nature of the charges against her. Thomas Cromwell, who was instructed to take care of the legal formalities, was hoping that Anne would incriminate her circle of friends. When the Queen learned that she was accused of adultery, she protested her innocence. "I can say but nay without I should open my body", she told Kingston and made a dramatic, biblical gesture of tugging at the front of her gown.[6] Just as Cromwell hoped, Anne started to babble nervously, and the women who served her ("such as I never loved", Anne complained) reported everything to Kingston.

The Queen must have known that Sir Henry Norris, the King's friend and an honourable member of the Privy Chamber, was accused with her. "Oh! Norris hast thou accused me?" she wailed. "Thou art in the Tower with me, and thou and I shall die together".[7] She suspected that a conversation she had with him on the last weekend of April had been misconstrued and used against them to prove something sinister was happening between them. One day Anne berated Norris for not marrying her cousin Mary Shelton. Norris replied that he was not in a hurry, and Anne retorted that he was looking to marry her if the King died. This was later used to prove that Anne and Norris had been lovers and plotted the King's death. Yet Norris was not the only man accused of being her putative lover. Mark Smeaton, the talented courtly musician, confessed that he had intercourse with Anne on three different occasions. Whether he was tortured or promised pardon is unclear.

The trial of Anne Boleyn's brother, who was accused of committing incest with her on several occasions, was a scandalous one and sealed his fate. Thomas Cromwell passed George Boleyn a piece of paper with a warning not to read it aloud. George disregarded this warning and made the statement public, enraging Cromwell, who clearly wanted to keep it secret. According to the message written on the parchment, Anne Boleyn told George's wife, Jane, that the King *"nestoit habile en cas de soy copuler avec femme, et quil navoit ne vertu ne puissance"*.[8] It was a highly intimate detail from behind the closed doors of the royal bedchamber. It was so intimate and shocking that the nineteenth-century translator of *Letters and Papers* did not bother to translate it in full but included only its original French version (as written down by the imperial ambassador Chapuys, whose native language was French), hoping that the reader would figure its meaning for himself.

What Anne said can be translated as follows: "The King was not capable of copulating with a woman because he had neither virtue nor potency." This comment strongly implied that her husband suffered from bouts of impotency.

Perhaps he did; during his fourth marriage, the King admitted so himself when he said he was unable to have sex with Anne of Cleves, whom he thought was supremely unattractive, but didn't have problems with other women.

In the sixteenth-century mind-set, the fact that Anne Boleyn entertained doubts about Henry's potency cast a shadow of doubt on her own morals, not Henry's. The implication was clear: if the King was impotent, who was the father of Anne's daughter? Perhaps this is how we should look upon Chapuys's report that George Boleyn was charged with spreading "reports which called in question whether his sister's daughter was the King's child".[9] In light of Anne's remark that Henry was impotent, George's words must surely have been intended as a bawdy joke referring to the King's lack of prowess in bed. To this charge, he made no answer.

Anne's confession may have been a mere boast, a joke reflecting her frustration and impatience with waiting for another pregnancy. In fact, we don't know much about her confession except that she confided in her sister-in-law, Jane Boleyn. During his trial, George Boleyn turned to the peers who judged him and said it was unreasonable that "on the evidence of only one woman you are willing to believe this great evil of me, and on the basis of her allegations you are deciding my judgment".[10] For centuries, historians believed he was referring to his own wife, Jane, yet he mentioned "one woman" without revealing who she was. In the late sixteenth century, George Wyatt poured scorn on Jane, writing:

"For this principal matter between the Queen and her brother, there was brought forth, indeed, witness, his wicked wife accuser of her own husband, even to the seeking of his own blood, which I believe is hardly to be showed of any honest woman ever done."[11]

Latching on to Wyatt's description, Bishop Gilbert Burnet in 1649 described Jane as a "spiteful wife" who "carried many stories to the King, or some about him, to persuade, that there was a familiarity between the Queen and her brother, beyond what so near a relation could justify".[12] Jane's exaggerated role in Anne Boleyn's downfall is based on her own tragic end: she was executed for facilitating Katherine Howard's meetings with Thomas Culpeper in 1542. In fact, both Wyatt and Burnet mentioned Jane's execution when writing about her alleged role in Anne's fall, pointing out that her own scandalous death must have been divine retribution. The whole record of Anne's trial is now lost, but it's certain that her ladies-in-waiting were interrogated and provided false testimonies. Jane Boleyn wasn't mentioned among the "first accusers" of the Queen. She gained nothing after the deaths of her sister-in-law and husband and returned to court only after begging Cromwell to help her.

Years later George Constantine, one of Henry Norris's servants, reminisced that he had heard opinions that George Boleyn would have escaped death "had it not been for a letter". The "letter" in this context may have been understood as a literal letter or a document. Constantine may have been referring to the piece of parchment with his wife's confession handed to George Boleyn during the trial.[13] Writing in the early reign of Queen Elizabeth I, Scottish theologian Alexander Alesius wrote that Anne's enemies were in possession of letters wherein Anne informed her brother that she was pregnant.[14] He added that during the trial:

"The Queen was accused of having danced in the bedroom with the gentlemen of the King's chamber and of having kissed her brother, Lord Rochford. When she made no answer to these accusations, the King's syndic or proctor, Master Polwarck, produced certain letters and bawled out that she could not deny she had written to her brother, informing him that she was pregnant. Still she continued silent."[15]

The letters wherein Anne informed her brother that she was pregnant could have been produced during her trial, but even if they were, writing such letters announcing pregnancy wasn't seen as scandalous in itself. Alesius pointed out that it was customary "with young women to write to their near relatives when they have become pregnant, in order to receive their congratulations".[16] Anne's contemporaries certainly did that and were never accused of sexual improprieties on that account. Marguerite of Navarre, sister of Francis I of France, wrote a very private letter to Anne de Montmorency, Great Master of France, informing him that her "monthly period is eight days overdue, which is very unusual for me. I do not dare to announce it, for fear that it may be nothing; yet that is why I am afraid to start out".[17]

Lurid, fanciful details about Anne's alleged incestuous relations with her brother were added to the indictment against her. On 2 November 1535, she was said to have "procured and incited" him "to violate her, alluring him with her tongue in the said George's mouth, and the said George's tongue in hers, and also with kisses, presents, and jewels". Reciprocating Anne's insinuations and "despising the commands of God, and all human laws", George "violated and carnally knew the said Queen, his own sister, at Westminster" on 5 November 1535. They had sex, the indictment claimed, "on divers other days before and after at the same place, sometimes by his own procurement and sometimes by the Queen's".[18]

Eustace Chapuys, Anne's grand enemy, could not believe these charges. As much as he despised Anne for her evangelical beliefs and for usurping Katharine of Aragon's place, he admitted: "Her brother was charged with having cohabited with her by presumption, because he had been once found a long time with her, and with certain other little follies." A seasoned lawyer with an eye for detail, he marvelled that "no witnesses were produced against either him or her, as it is usual to do, particularly when the accused denies the charge".[19]

Other men accused as Anne's lovers were said to have been sleeping with her on many occasions, but that was not all. They were charged with conspiring "the death and destruction of the King, the Queen often saying she would marry one of them as soon as the King died, and affirming that she would never love the King in her heart".[20]

Anne remained calm throughout her trial and denied the charges. She owned up to having been jealous, volatile and insecure, but she made it luminously clear that she was not an adulteress:

"I do not say that I always borne towards the King the humility which I owed him, considering his kindness and the great honour he showed me and the great respect he always paid me; I admit, too, that often I have taken it into my head to be jealous of him . . . But may God be my witness if I have done him any other wrong."[21]

The men also pleaded their innocence, with the exception of Mark Smeaton, who said he had sex with Anne on three occasions. It's possible that he was tortured or promised a pardon. Off all the five men executed as Anne's lovers, Mark was of the lowest social position. A musician, not a gentleman of the Privy Chamber, he was the only one who could have been legally tortured.

Anne herself seemed to have believed she would survive. The day after her trial, she was "in hope of life" when the Archbishop of Canterbury visited her.[22] Yet two days later Anne was told she must prepare to die. The execution was originally scheduled to take place on 18 May, but a delay occurred, much to Anne's distress. On the morning of 19 May 1536, Anne made a short walk from her luxurious apartments in the Tower to the high scaffold prepared for her execution. She made a brief but powerful speech, asking the assembled crowd to pray for her soul and for the King, "for a gentler nor a more merciful prince was there never".[23] She was beheaded with a clean stroke of the French executioner's sword.

And what about Henry? Did he believe that Anne was guilty, or did he order her judicial murder with premeditation? Chapuys later wrote that Thomas Cromwell took credit for Anne's downfall:

"He, himself had been authorised and commissioned by the King to prosecute and bring to an end the mistress's trial, to do which he had taken considerable trouble. It was he who, in consequence of the disappointment and anger he had felt on hearing the King's answer to me on the third day of Easter, had planned and brought about the whole affair."[24]

The King as well gave out hints that he had known about Anne's downfall in advance. As Anne was awaiting her fate in the Tower, Henry dined with several ladies at the house of the Bishop of Carlisle and "manifested incredible joy at the arrest of Anne". Chapuys, who spoke with the bishop, wrote:

"Indeed, he related to me that, among other topics of conversation, the King touched on that of the concubine, saying: 'For a long time back had I predicted what would be the end of this affair, so much so that I have written a tragedy, which I have here by me.' Saying which, he took out of his breast pocket a small book all written in his own hand and handed it over to the Bishop, who, however, did not examine its contents."[25]

On his deathbed eleven years later, Henry was said to have expressed "peculiar remorse for the wrong he had done Anne Boleyn by putting her to death on a false accusation".[26] This was recorded by the contemporary Franciscan French monk André Thevet, who resided in England at that time.

NOTES

1 *Letters and Papers, Foreign and Domestic, Henry VIII,* Volume 10, n. 352.
2 Ibid., Volume 4, n. 3913.
3 Ibid., Volume 10, n. 876.
4 *Calendar of State Papers, Spain,* Volume 5 Part 2, n. 55.
5 Eric Ives, *The Life and Death of Anne Boleyn*, p. 349.
6 *Letters and Papers, Foreign and Domestic, Henry VIII,* Volume 10, n. 793.
7 Ibid.

[8] Ibid., n. 908.
[9] Ibid.
[10] Eric Ives, *The Life and Death of Anne Boleyn*, p. 331.
[11] Extracts from George Wyatt's *Life of Anne Boleigne* printed in George Cavendish, *The Life and Death of Cardinal Wolsey*, p. 446.
[12] Gilbert Burnet, *Bishop Burnet's History of the Reformation of the Church of England, Volume 1*, p. 306.
[13] T. Amyot (ed.), "A memorial from George Constantine", in *Archaeologia*, 23 (1831), p. 66.
[14] *Calendar of State Papers Foreign: Elizabeth,* Volume 1, 1558-1559, n. 1303.
[15] Ibid., 1303 (25).
[16] Ibid., 1303 (28).
[17] Patricia F. Cholakian and Rouben C. Cholakian, *Marguerite de Navarre: Mother of the Renaissance*, p. 141.
[18] *Letters and Papers, Foreign and Domestic, Henry VIII,* Volume 10, n. 876 (7).
[19] Ibid., n. 908.
[20] Ibid., Volume 10, n. 876 (7).
[21] Eric Ives, *The Life and Death of Anne Boleyn*, p. 341.
[22] *Letters and Papers, Foreign and Domestic, Henry VIII,* Volume 10, n. 890.
[23] Raphael Holinshed, *Holinshed's Chronicles of England, Scotland and Ireland*, Volume 3, p. 797.
[24] *Calendar of State Papers, Spain,* Volume 5 Part 2, n. 61.
[25] Ibid., n. 55.
[26] Agnes Strickland, *Lives of the Queens of England*, Volume 2, p. 271.

CHAPTER 13: "CUT OUT OF HER WOMB"

On 30 May 1536 Jane Seymour married not a divorced man, but a wife-murderer. The court was plunged into a series of entertainments and lavish banquets, as if celebrating Henry VIII's new life without Anne. During the wedding celebrations of the Earl of Rutland's children, the King gave everyone a reason to doubt his sanity when he made his appearance dressed up as an infidel Turk.

Celebratory jousts and weddings of court members were attended by the King and his new wife, but the death of Henry's illegitimate son, Henry FitzRoy, on 22 July 1536 put a dramatic stop to the celebrations. Born in June 1519, the seventeen-year-old FitzRoy was the apple of Henry's eye. Following Anne Boleyn's execution, Henry even contemplated legitimizing FitzRoy and placing him in the line of succession in case Jane Seymour proved barren. Edward Hall called FitzRoy "a goodly man child, of beauty like to the father and mother".[1] Henry Fitzroy was painted by Lucas Horenbout; in his miniature, he appears to be dressed informally in a linen shirt, with the high collar left undone, and a close-fitting embroidered cap. Fitzroy's resemblance to Henry VIII is striking; he has grey eyes, pale skin and reddish eyebrows. Contemporaries often remarked upon Fitzroy's resemblance to Henry VIII; he was described as "a youth of great promise, so much does he resemble his father".[2]

Little is known of Henry FitzRoy's last illness; there's no evidence that he was sickly. Eustace Chapuys recorded that FitzRoy had been "in a state of rapid consumption", and, according to his physicians, he could not live many more months.[3] FitzRoy's untimely death spurred gossip that he had been poisoned. The contemporary chronicle of the Windsor Herald recorded that "it was thought that he was privily [secretly] poisoned by the means of Queen Anne [Boleyn] and her brother, Lord Rochford, for he pined inwardly in his body long before he died".[4]

In an age before forensic science, poison was usually suspected whenever a young, healthy person died unexpectedly. During Anne Boleyn's trial, she was accused of planning to poison Katharine of Aragon and Princess Mary, and following her arrest Henry VIII told FitzRoy that "he and his sister, meaning the Princess [Mary], were greatly bound to God for having escaped the hands of that accursed whore [Anne], who had determined to poison them".[5]

People in the sixteenth century believed in poisons that worked over a long period of time, and indeed some poisons, if administered in small doses over extended periods, could kill slowly. Yet by the time of FitzRoy's death, Anne Boleyn had been dead for two months, so a slow-acting poison administered by her seems unlikely. Also, the charges of poisoning were most likely fabricated; although Anne bragged about poisoning her enemies on several occasions, she never acted upon her words.

FitzRoy's death plunged Henry VIII into a state of depression. In November 1536, the King was complaining that "since the Queen would not give him a son", he would finally consider marrying his elder daughter, Mary, to some Habsburg princeling to prolong the Tudor dynasty through her, as Chapuys had brazenly suggested in 1533. But the King was being overdramatic. He always wanted everything right away, like a spoilt child. Anne Boleyn had become pregnant in what may have been her first full sexual encounter with Henry in late 1532, and she conceived another child two months after Elizabeth's birth. Fertility was not her problem. Neither was it Jane Seymour's, apparently. Henry VIII clearly expected her to become pregnant right away, but it took the couple eight months to conceive.

Psychological pressure may have contributed to Jane's stress, impacting her childbearing ability, and the dramatic situation of that summer contributed to the royal couple's ineffective performance in bed. The year 1536 is often said to have been Henry VIII's *annus horribilis*: Not only was Anne Boleyn executed, but shortly afterwards Henry Fitzroy died, and a rebellion in the northern part of the country broke out later that summer, creating one of the biggest challenges of Henry VIII's reign. It is no wonder that the King became depressed and started entertaining doubts as to his potency and Jane Seymour's ability to bear children.

Yet in early May 1537, rumours had it that Jane was twenty weeks pregnant.[6] She could no longer hide her pregnancy and planned to go "open-laced with stomacher" on the Corpus Christi Day feast in June.[7] Pregnant women during the Tudor era signified their condition by unlacing their stomachers—decorative pieces worn under the front lacing of the bodice. On 27 May, Jane's baby moved inside her belly; this "quickening" was celebrated throughout the country with *Te Deums* sung in churches, bonfires lit in the streets and wine poured out of hogsheads distributed for free among the poor by nobility.[8]

Jane Seymour established her birthing chamber at the newly refurbished Hampton Court Palace, breaking with the tradition of royal children being born at Greenwich. She took to her chamber on 27 September while the King left for Esher Place, a few miles from Hampton Court. On 10 October 1537, the Queen went into labour that dragged for longer than anticipated, and on 11 October a solemn procession went through London "to pray for the Queen that was then in labour of child".[9] Finally, at two o'clock in the morning of 12 October 1537, Jane Seymour succeeded where her predecessor had failed and gave birth to a healthy baby boy. Three days later Prince Edward, named after the saint on whose feast day he was born, was baptised in the royal chapel at Hampton Court, with the nobility and the King's daughters present for the occasion.

Yet soon after the christening, the Queen's health deteriorated. Day by day, she grew increasingly weak until, on 23 October 1537, she had "a natural lax" after which it looked like she was on the road to full recovery.[10] This "natural lax" was not a "heavy bleeding", as suggested by Edward VI's biographer.[11] "Lax", in the medical context of the era, meant diarrhoea. But Jane's condition worsened at night, and in the morning her confessor administered the extreme unction. She was "very sick" and attended by three of the King's chief physicians: John Chambre, William Butts and George Owen.[12] Thomas Howard, Duke of Norfolk, despatched a quick note to Thomas Cromwell, advising him "to be here tomorrow early to comfort our good master, for as for our mistress there is no likelihood of her life". He ended: "I fear she shall not be alive at the time ye shall read this."[13] Norfolk was right. Jane Seymour died on 24 October 1537 at Hampton Court Palace. Was Henry VIII at her deathbed? Much is made of the fact that the King planned to leave Hampton Court while Jane was dying, but closer examination of the sources clearly shows that her death caused him much pain. On 24 October, shortly before Jane's death, Sir John Russell wrote to Cromwell informing him of the King's whereabouts:

"The King was determined, as this day, to have removed to Esher; and because the Queen was very sick this night, and this day, he tarried; but tomorrow, God willing, he intended to be there. If she amends, he will go; but if she amends not, he told me, this day, 'he could not find it in his heart'; for, I assure you, she hath been in great danger yesternight and this day. Thanked be God, she is somewhat amended; and if she escapes this night, the physicians be in good hope that she be past all danger."[14]

It appears that Henry was at Hampton Court when Jane breathed her last; whether he was at her deathbed remains possible but unlikely, considering his inherent dread of sickness and death. It may be that Jane's premature death reawakened unpleasant memories of the death of Henry's beloved mother, who died in similar circumstances thirty-four years earlier. Chronicler Edward Hall wrote that following Jane's death Henry departed to Westminster Palace "where he mourned and kept himself close and secret a great while".[15] This is not entirely correct because on the day of Jane's death Henry returned to Esher Place.

Before the end of October, Henry met with his councillors there and, according to Cromwell, was convinced to remarry. The King apparently "took pleasure" at Esher, and Cromwell implied that Henry could request it as a gift from Stephen Gardiner, Bishop of Winchester. Esher was the property of Gardiner's see, and the bishop ceded the estate to the King, albeit reluctantly and not without regret.[16] Gardiner wrote plainly to Cromwell that he didn't want to part with Esher, but Cromwell chided the bishop, saying that the King's sojourn there wasn't merely for fun and games; it was a place "where there is a grief", implying that the King closeted himself away from court at Esher to mourn Jane Seymour's death.[17] It was probably from Esher that the King wrote a letter to Francis I of France, informing him that "Divine Providence has mingled my joy with the bitterness of the death of her who brought me to this happiness".[18]

Clearly, Henry wasn't entirely without company; he kept seeing his councillors and talked about remarrying. "The King is in good health and merry as a widower may be, the Prince also", wrote Sir John Wallop to Lord Lisle on 3 November.[19] The Queen was buried on 12 November at St George's Chapel at Windsor with great pomp and solemnity, with her ladies-in-waiting and household officers present.

Some years after Jane's death, tales started spreading that in order to extract Prince Edward from her belly, a Caesarean cut was performed. William Camden, the first biographer of Queen Elizabeth I, wrote that "Queen Jane fell ill in labour of Prince Edward, and presently died, the said Prince being fain to be cut out of her womb".[20] Nicholas Sander, writing in 1581, claimed that "the travail of the Queen being very difficult, the King was asked which of the two lives was to be spared; he answered, the boy's, because he could easily provide himself with other wives."[21] This account assumes that Henry knew in advance that Jane was about to give birth to a son and could be easily dismissed as fanciful since the King could not have had such knowledge prior to his child's birth. Sander's narrative is in general very hostile towards the King and paints him as a bloodthirsty villain who mistreated his wives and broke with the Catholic Church because he was lusting after his second wife, Anne Boleyn.

While it true that Jane Seymour's labour was very long and exhaustive, there is no truth in the tales about a Caesarean birth. She was well enough to participate in her son's post-christening reception on 15 October; although the royal parents did not take part in the christening itself, they awaited their infant son in an antechamber decorated for the occasion. The Queen started to feel ill shortly after the christening, falling in and out of consciousness. Thomas Cromwell blamed Jane's death on "the neglect of those about her who suffered her to take cold and eat such things as her fantasy in sickness called for".[22] Two years after Jane's death rumours circulated abroad that she was "lost for lack of keeping in her childbed".[23] It's more likely that she died of complications that arose after prolonged labour.

Historians usually ascribe Jane's death to heavy bleeding caused by retention of part of the placenta.[24]

NOTES

[1] Alison Weir, *Henry VIII: King and Court*, p. 220.
[2] Ibid.
[3] *Calendar of State Papers, Spain,* Volume 5 Part 2, n. 71.
[4] *Wriothesley's Chronicle,* Volume 1, pp. 53-4.
[5] *Letters and Papers, Foreign and Domestic, Henry VIII,* Volume 10, n. 908.
[6] *Letters and Papers, Foreign and Domestic, Henry VIII,* Volume 12 Part 1, n. 1164, 1165.
[7] Ibid., n. 1267.
[8] Wriothesley's Chronicle, Volume 1, p. 64.
[9] Ibid, p. 65.
[10] *State Papers*, Volume 1, p. 572.
[11] Jennifer Loach, *Edward VI*, p. 7.
[12] *State Papers*, Volume 1, p. 572.
[13] *Letters and Papers, Foreign and Domestic, Henry VIII,* Volume 12 Part 2, n. 971.
[14] Agnes Strickland, Elisabeth Strickland, *Lives of the Queens of England, from the Norman Conquest*, Volume 2, p. 285.
[15] Edward Hall, *Hall's Chronicle*, p. 825.
[16] Roger Merriman, *Life and Letters of Thomas Cromwell*, Volume 2, p. 98.
[17] Ibid.
[18] *Letters and Papers, Foreign and Domestic, Henry VIII,* Volume 12 Part 2, n. 972.
[19] Ibid., n. 1023.
[20] William Camden, *The History of the Most Renowned and Victorious Princess Elizabeth*, p. 5.
[21] Nicholas Sander, *The Rise and Growth of the Anglican Schism*, p. 138.
[22] *Letters and Papers, Foreign and Domestic, Henry VIII,* Volume 12 Part 2, n. 1004.
[23] Ibid., Volume 14 Part 2, n. 400.
[24] Jennifer Loach, *Edward VI*, p. 7.

CHAPTER 14: "LOOSENESS OF HER BREASTS"

On 1 January 1540, Henry VIII couldn't have been more excited. Just three days earlier a woman who was to become his fourth wife had set foot on English soil. Their first meeting had been scheduled to take place on 3 January, but the King was so impatient he decided to ride at breakneck speed from Greenwich Palace in London to Rochester Castle in Kent, where his bride was staying. The King had only seen a portrait of Anne of Cleves painted by Hans Holbein, his court artist, who had been despatched to Anne's native duchy of Cleves because Henry didn't trust anyone else to convey her likeness. Holbein was one of the most skilled artists of his day, painting his subjects with a lifelike precision, and he proved his worth when he painted the King and his third wife, Jane Seymour, in 1536.

Scouring European courts for his fourth bride, in 1538 Henry asked the French ambassador to gather the ladies offered by Francis I, King of France, in Calais, so that Henry could inspect them. "It is not the custom in France to send damsels of that rank and of such noble and princely families to be passed in review as if they were hackneys for sale", the French king scoffed when the English ambassador conveyed Henry's message.[1] "I trust no one but myself", Henry told the bemused French ambassador, "the thing touches me too near. I wish to see them and know them some time before deciding".[2] This answer encapsulated Henry VIII's views on marriage, love and courtship; he wanted a perfect bride, someone he could fall in love with. If only he could see his future wife. But that was impossible, and Henry's request appeared ridiculous in the eyes of his peers, who mostly married for political gain. The French Queen even quipped that "she was not the keeper of harlots" to parade them for Henry's amusement.[3] Unable to inspect his future bride himself, the King instructed his ambassadors to be his eyes and ears.

After sifting through descriptions and portraits of various candidates, Henry's attention was caught by his ambassadors' enthusiastic praises of Lady Anne of Cleves. Born on 22 September 1515 to John III, Duke of Cleves, and Maria of Jülich-Berg, Anne was of similar age to Henry's daughter Mary. Raised under the auspices of her strict mother, Anne knew how to read and write, but wasn't taught to dance, sing or play musical instruments "for they take it here in Germany for a rebuke and an occasion of lightness that great ladies should be learned or have any knowledge of music".[4] She also spoke no other language than her native German. The English ambassadors "praised the beauty" of the twenty-four-year-old lady "as well for the face, as for the whole body, above all other ladies excellent".[5] Hans Holbein painted her in her native red-and-gold German dress, accentuating Anne's slim waistline, her hazel eyes, dreamy half-smile and beringed hands clasped humbly in front of her. When the King saw the portrait, he was delighted.

Anne arrived in England on 29 December 1539 after a long and perilous sea crossing. Henry VIII decided to ride to Rochester Castle, one of many stops on Anne's way towards London, because he "desired to see her Grace" very much. The King decided to surprise Anne and hide his identity, visiting her in her apartments disguised as a royal messenger, surrounded by eight members of his Privy Chamber.

Dressing up played an important part in courtly gallantry, and Henry, reared on chivalrous tales about the Knights of the Round Table, was used to playing such charades with his first wife. When the door to her apartments opened, Anne of Cleves stood by the window, watching a bear baiting—in which a bear was chained to a post and set on by dogs—when the hooded Henry approached her and suddenly embraced and kissed her, presenting a gift from the King. Anne was supposed to recognise him instantly by the virtue of his kingly office and appearance, but she failed to do so and "regarded him little", paying more attention to the bloody spectacle unfolding just outside her window than to the ruddy giant of a man who stood in front of her.[6] The King's face showed signs of "discontentment and misliking of her person" and "he tarried not to speak with her twenty words". The rich gifts Henry brought with him were not delivered at this time but sent the next morning by Sir Anthony Browne of the Privy Chamber with a "cold message" from the King.[7]

One wonders how was it possible that Anne of Cleves failed to recognise the King. He was a distinctive-looking man, so tall he was towering over his courtiers, and so massive that he had to support his weight on a walking staff. Portrait exchange was part of the courtship ritual, and so it seems near impossible that Anne wasn't shown a portrait of the King. It's even possible that when Hans Holbein painted her, he showed her the portrait of Henry he himself had painted in 1536; this was the most recent painting of Henry and one that the King was very proud of. Is it possible that Henry looked nothing like Holbein's portrait? The painting suggests the sitter to be strong, healthy and virile, but Henry was anything but in 1539.

In his youth, Henry VIII was one of the best-looking princes in Europe. In 1515, when he was twenty-four years old, the Venetian ambassador wrote that:

"The King is the handsomest potentate I ever set eyes on; above the usual height, with an extremely fine calf to his leg, his complexion very fair and bright, with auburn hair combed straight and short, in the French fashion, and a round face so very beautiful that it would become a pretty woman, his throat being rather long and thick."[8]

Apart from his impressive physique, the ambassador praised Henry's language skills and sport activities:

"He speaks French, English and Latin, and a little Italian; plays well on the lute and harpsichord, sings from book at sight, draws the bow with greater strength than any man in England and jousts marvellously."[9]

Henry VIII was apparently a very attractive youth, but his physique started to change in 1526. A miniature of Henry at the age of thirty-five survives and depicts him as a beardless, slightly overweight man, with his auburn hair showing from under a black cap. In 1531, Henry was described by another Venetian diplomat in the following words:

"His face is angelic rather than handsome; his head imperial like Caesar's and bald, and he wears a beard, contrary to English custom. Who would not be amazed when contemplating such singular corporal beauty, coupled with such bold address, adapting itself with the greatest ease to every manly exercise? He sits his horse well, and manages him yet better; he jousts and wields his spear, throws the quoit, and draws the bow, admirably; plays at tennis most dexterously; and nature having endowed him in youth with such gifts, he was not slow to enhance, preserve and augment them with all industry and labour."[10]

Yet by 1540 Henry was no longer the athletic young prince who had ascended the throne so many years ago. He was now a limping and grossly overweight shadow of the man he used to be and looked nothing like a King without his golden crown and rich attire. The injuries to his legs sustained during his last jousting accident in 1536 marked the rapid decline of his health. In June 1537, he called off his intended northern progress because "a humour has fallen into our legs and our physicians advise us not to go so far in the heat of the year".[11] The King's legs had a tendency to swell, and they were covered in fistulas. In 1538, one of the fistulas closed up, and the King remained speechless for almost two weeks, "black in the face and in great danger".[12] The royal physicians lanced the fistula with a red-hot poker, allowing drainage of the "humours" and saving the King's life. From that point on, the fistulas were kept open for the King's safety, producing a putrid stench that could be identified three rooms away, often announcing Henry's arrival. Baron Montague, one of Henry's enemies, remarked that "the King is full of flesh and unwieldly, and that he cannot long continue with his sore leg".[13]

Thus it may have been a shock to Anne of Cleves when she saw Henry VIII for the first time. Seeing the lack of interest in his person on Anne's part, the King left her and returned dressed in a splendid cloak of purple velvet. This time everyone bowed when he entered, and Anne, speechless at the sight, fell on her knees in stony silence. Although they talked a while, neither of them could forget the awkward first impressions that were now etched in their hearts and minds. From the very first moment he saw Anne of Cleves, Henry VIII was determined to avoid their wedding. "I see nothing in this woman as men report of her", he told Sir Anthony Browne of the Privy Chamber as they made their way back from Rochester to Greenwich.[14] When the King asked Sir John Russell, Lord Admiral, who saw Anne in Rochester, whether "he thought the woman so fair and of such beauty as report had been made of her", the admiral replied that she was not "fair" but of a "brown complexion".[15] Considering that Henry was so disgusted with Anne's appearance, the admiral's comment seems unrevealing. All he could say about this woman who was to become the next Queen of England was that her complexion was not pale, but this was hardly a surprise considering that Holbein's portrait clearly showed that Anne of Cleves's skin was not snowy white, and Henry had been able to fall in love with olive-skinned women in the past. Several historians repeated over the years that Anne's face was covered with smallpox scars, but there's no evidence for this. Although smallpox scars were common at the time, they were often remarked upon, and so it seems unlikely that they would pass without any comment. The only contemporary criticism levelled against Anne was that she looked "about thirty years of age, [was] tall and thin, of medium beauty, and of very assured and resolute countenance."[16] Chronicler Edward Hall was enthusiastic, musing that Anne was "so fair a lady of so goodly a stature and so womanly a countenance."[17] Nicander Nucius of

Corfu, who visited England in 1545 and wrote an account of his travels in classical Greek, recorded that Anne was "a masculine woman, and of great beauty."[18] Whether he based his observation after seeing Anne or was repeating gossip is unknown.

"Alas, whom should men trust?" the King mused pensively. "I see no such thing in her as hath been showed unto me of her, and am ashamed that men hath so praised her as they have done, and I like her not, he said".[19] It's been suggested by some historians that Hans Holbein flattered Anne and that she looked nothing like his portrait. This seems not to be the case, as the English ambassador who saw Anne in person commented that Holbein's painting was a close likeness.[20]

Yet whether he liked her or not, things had gone too far since Anne was already in England and couldn't be sent back to Cleves. The wedding ceremony was first scheduled to take place on 4 January, but the King deferred it in the hope of finding an impediment. At this stage, Henry VIII was desperately looking for a way out of his commitment to Anne of Cleves. Could, perhaps, her pre-contract to the Duke of Lorraine be used as obstacle to their union, he wondered? A pre-contract, or a marriage agreement, was drawn when two parties or their representatives agreed to marry. In some cases, pre-contracts could be dissolved, but if they were consummated, they were often deemed indissoluble. The King now believed that Anne had been pre-contracted to another man before she came to England and demanded to see the paperwork stating that she was free to marry. The representatives of Anne's brother, Duke William of Cleves, declared to the King that Anne was free to marry, but they possessed no documentation that cleared her from any previous pre-contract. They made "a light matter of it", saying that the pre-contract between Anne and the Duke of Lorraine was "done in their minority and had never taken any effect".[21] In other words, the marriage negotiations never went any further than words and empty promises, and there was no documentation because no formal marriage contract had ever been drawn between Anne of Cleves and the Duke of Lorraine. Henry VIII was furious because the pre-contract was his only way out of the abhorred marriage. The King found himself in a situation where he had no control over his future. Confiding in his principal secretary Thomas Cromwell, who was the architect of the Cleves marriage, Henry said:

"If it were not that she is come so far into my realm and the great preparations that my states and my people have made for her and for fear of making a ruffle in the world—that is to mean to drive her brother into the hands of the Emperor and the French King's hands, being now together [allied], I would never have her, but now it is so far gone."[22]

The King hoped that if a delegation of his privy councillors visited Anne and asked her to swear an oath that she was bound by no other marriage contracts, she might say something that could be used to avoid the marriage. Yet Anne swore that she was never pre-contracted or even if she were, the pre-contract was null and void as it had never progressed beyond words. Did Anne feel that something was amiss? Why would the King's men ask her such things just before their marriage? When Henry learned of Anne's oath, he cried out: "Is there none other remedy, but that I must needs, against my will, put my neck in the yoke?" The wedding plans went ahead, and the couple tied the knot on 6 January 1540. Awaiting Anne in a presence chamber on the morning preceding their wedding, Henry scolded Cromwell, saying: "My lord, if it were not to satisfy the world and my realm, I would not do that I must do this day, for none earthly thing."[23] Henry had to pretend that all was well, but in reality he was already planning the annulment of his fourth marriage.

On her wedding day, Anne wore her "fair, yellow and long" hair loose, as unmarried women did during that period. A rich "gold coronet of gemstones and pearls" set with branches of rosemary adorned her head. Her gown of cloth of silver was sparkling with "great Oriental pearls" and jewels.[24] The King, to whom she curtsied three times, after the custom of her country, cut a striking figure in his black fur-trimmed gown of cloth of gold beneath a cloak of crimson satin strewn with diamonds.

After the wedding banquet, Henry VIII and Anne of Cleves left the company and headed towards their nuptial bedchamber. The custom of witnessing the consummation of a royal marriage was only a distant memory, and after the ceremonial blessing of the marriage bed the crowd dispersed. Undressed by their intimate body servants, Anne and Henry were ceremoniously laid to bed next to each other, and the curtains were drawn. Only they knew what happened that night between them. Their wedding night can be reconstructed based on what Henry VIII told his servants and physicians, but it has to be remembered that this version of events paints Anne of Cleves in an unfavourable light because of the King's wish to annul their marriage. Anne's version of events was suppressed and embellished later to match it with the King's.

What occurred may never be known, but what is clear is that Henry put his hands on Anne's breasts, groping them clumsily, and moved lower to touch her private parts but felt no inclination to proceed any further. Kissing her on the forehead, he wished her good night and fell asleep. Emerging from the bedchamber he shared with his new wife early in the morning of 7 January, Henry VIII was in a foul mood. When Thomas Cromwell dared to ask him how he liked his new Queen, the King snapped: "Surely, you know, I liked her before not well, but now I like her much worse."[25]

Despite the fact that he visited Anne's bedchamber on the third and fourth night following their disastrous wedding, the King had already started a whispering campaign aimed against her. Whenever he emerged from Anne's bedchamber, Henry would complain to his closest male servants about her physique. Thomas Heneage, knight of the King's body, remembered that the King "often said plainly he mistrusted her to be no maid, by reason of the looseness of her breasts and other tokens". Heneage also recalled that the King spoke of how "he could have none appetite with her to do as a man should do with his wife, for such displeasing airs as he felt with her".[26] Sir Anthony

Denny, a trusted gentleman of the King's Privy Chamber, also testified that Henry:

"... could not induce himself to have affection for the Queen, for that she was not as what was reported, but had her breasts so slack, and other parts of body in such sort, that his Highness somewhat suspected her virginity, and concluded that her body was of such indisposition to his, that he could never in her company be provoked and stirred to know her carnally."[27]

The King was alarmed that he could not consummate his marriage with Anne; he had no erection and was thus unable to penetrate her. He confided to his doctors, Chambers and Butts, that he "found her body in such a sort disordered and indisposed to excite and provoke any lust in him" that he "could not in any wise overcome that loathsomeness, nor in her company be provoked or stirred to that act". But Henry, who was highly sensitive about his manhood, could not afford to claim that he was impotent—that would have been Anne Boleyn's last laugh from the grave. Rather, he told Dr Butts he had two wet dreams at night and believed himself "able to do the act with others but not with her".[28] So, yet again, Henry VIII blamed his wife for the failure of their marriage.

Anne must have known that something was amiss because she "often desired" to speak to Thomas Cromwell. Cromwell, however, dared not speak with the Queen about her marital problems, knowing only too well that discussing the King's sexual prowess could be sufficient grounds to lose one's head (hence the example of Anne Boleyn and her brother). Instead, he instructed the Queen's English ladies-in-waiting to provoke a discussion about the intimate secrets of the royal bedchamber. On one occasion, Ladies Rochford, Rutland and Edgecombe approached Anne and told her that they assumed she was still a virgin. How could this be, the Queen marvelled, if she slept every night with the King? Lady Rochford, herself a widow since 1536 and well versed in what was required of a married couple in bed, frankly told Anne that "there must be more than that" to lose one's virginity. Anne explained that apart from kissing her at night and in the morning, the King did not proceed any further. "Is this not enough?" she asked with a childlike naivety. "Madam, there must be more than this", Lady Rutland replied, "or otherwise we shall never get a Duke of York, which is what this kingdom is longing for".

Anne of Cleves's comments had been taken at face value and interpreted to mean that she had no idea what conjugal duties really entailed. Historian Elizabeth Norton challenged this notion in her biography of Anne of Cleves, pointing out that the Queen's knowledge of the English language was scant at the time—she still needed a translator to help her make sense of what the English delegates told her in July 1540, when the King sent them to acquaint Anne with his plans for divorcing her—and that the conversation might not have occurred at all.[29] It seems highly unlikely that Anne of Cleves, who was praised for her wit and intelligence, was unaware that a marriage must be consummated in order to be deemed legal and indissoluble, much less that she would talk about the King's sexual prowess with her English ladies-in-waiting. Interestingly, Anne's German confidante, Mrs Loew, was not asked to give a deposition concerning the Queen's marital life.

Although Anne was surprised that Henry found the means to annul their marriage, she decided to comply with his wishes. She already knew that her royal husband had a mistress who served as her maid of honour and was perhaps alarmed that if she didn't agree to the annulment she would end up banished like Katharine of Aragon or executed like Anne Boleyn. Although one seventeenth-century writer claimed that Anne fainted when the King's councillors visited her at Richmond Palace to inform her of the annulment, there's no evidence that she swooned or trembled. During her short tenure as Queen, Anne was dignified and well-mannered and remained so when she was informed that she was no longer Henry VIII's wife. Writing afterwards to her brother, the Duke of Cleves, she informed him "that my body remained in the integrity which I brought into this realm", which meant that she was still a virgin or at least wished to be perceived as such by the world.[30]

Anne's obedience was rewarded by the King, who wished to show that he wasn't such a bad husband after all. Anne was given a yearly allowance of £4,000 and a household full of servants so she didn't lack anything financially. She also received Richmond Palace and Hever Castle, as well as several smaller estates. Most importantly, she was given an honorary position within the royal family because the King "adopted me as his sister", which meant that Anne had precedence over all other women in England except Henry's Queen and his two daughters.[31]

Writing to Francis I, the French ambassador de Marillac stated that the English people "who loved and esteemed her much as the sweetest, most gracious and kindest Queen they ever had or would desire" regretted losing Anne of Cleves.[32]

NOTES

[1] *Calendar of State Papers, Spain,* Volume 6 Part 1, n. 4.
[2] *Letters and Papers, Foreign and Domestic, Henry VIII,* Volume 13 Part 2, n. 77.
[3] *Calendar of State Papers, Spain,* Volume 6 Part 1, n. 4.
[4] *Letters and Papers, Foreign and Domestic, Henry VIII,* Volume 14 Part 2, n. 33.
[5] *Letters and Papers, Foreign and Domestic, Henry VIII,* Volume 14 Part 1, n. 552.
[6] *Wriothesley's Chronicle,* Volume 1, pp. 109-110.
[7] Ibid., Volume 15, n. 7.
[8] Ibid., Volume 2, n. 395.
[9] Ibid.
[10] *Calendar of State Papers, Venice,* Volume 4, n. 694.
[11] *Letters and Papers, Foreign and Domestic, Henry VIII,* Volume 12 Part 2, n. 77.
[12] Ibid., Volume 13 Part 1, n. 995.
[13] Ibid., Volume 13 Part 2, n. 702.
[14] *Letters and Papers, Foreign and Domestic, Henry VIII,* Volume 15, n. 7.
[15] Ibid., n. 6.
[16] Ibid., n. 22, 23.
[17] Sarah Beth Watkins, *Anne of Cleves,* p. 52.
[18] *The Second Book of the Travels of Nicander Nucius of Corcyra* (ed. and trans. by J.A. Cramer), p. 49.
[19] *Letters and Papers, Foreign and Domestic, Henry VIII,* Volume 15, n. 6.
[20] Ibid., Volume 14 Part 2, n. 33.
[21] John Strype, *Ecclesiastical Memorials,* p. 452.
[22] Ibid.
[23] *Letters and Papers, Foreign and Domestic, Henry VIII,* Volume 15, n. 823.
[24] *Hall's Chronicle,* pp. 836-837.
[25] *Letters and Papers, Foreign and Domestic, Henry VIII,* Volume 15, n. 823.
[26] John Strype, *Ecclesiastical Memorials,* p. 458.
[27] Ibid., p. 459.
[28] Ibid., p. 461.
[29] Elizabeth Norton, *Anne of Cleves,* p. 74.
[30] *Letters and Papers, Foreign and Domestic, Henry VIII,* Volume 15, n. 898.
[31] Ibid., n. 898, 899.

[32] Ibid., n. 901.

CHAPTER 15: "MEDDLE WITH A MAN"

During his annulment proceedings with Anne of Cleves, Henry VIII wanted to make sure that no one would think that he was impotent because his impotency was only temporary and caused by the lack of physical attraction to his current wife. Within six months, the King's fourth marriage was annulled and he was able to remarry. When Henry told Dr Butts that he was able to make love to other women, he may have been telling the truth. As his marriage to Anne of Cleves was rapidly heading toward its end, the King was already in a relationship with Katherine Howard.

Katherine was the daughter of Edmund Howard and Jocasta Culpeper. Both of her parents were dead at the time the King married her, but Katherine had other, more powerful relatives still living. Through her father, she was a member of the powerful Howard family that grew to prominence during Henry VIII's reign. Katherine's step-grandmother was Agnes Howard, Dowager Duchess of Norfolk, who brought Katherine up in her household. There was also Thomas Howard, 3rd Duke of Norfolk, Katherine's paternal uncle and a great favourite of the King's. Katherine also had a host of cousins, aunts and uncles who were equally well-placed at court and held in great esteem by the King.

Katherine was considerably younger than Henry VIII. The exact year of her birth remains unknown, but the available evidence strongly suggests the date of 1522 or 1523.[1] People who saw her believed she was in her teens. The anonymous author of the Spanish *Henry VIII's Chronicle* remarked that Katherine "was not more than fifteen" at the time of her marriage.[2] Charles de Marillac, French ambassador at the Tudor court who knew Katherine, believed she was about eighteen when she married the King. All observers unanimously agreed that Katherine was a good-looking young lady. She was "more graceful and beautiful than any lady in the court" in the words of the anonymous Spanish chronicler and "rather graceful than beautiful, of short stature" according to de Marillac.[3]

Katherine Howard came to court at some point in late 1539 to serve as Anne of Cleves's maid of honour. Service at court was the highest privilege a noblewoman could aspire to and Katherine was happy to be able to carve out a career. Service at court also brought Katherine into Henry VIII's orbit, and the King quickly noticed the beautiful young maid of his wife. She embodied everything the ageing monarch valued in a woman: beauty, vivaciousness, wit and talent for courtly entertainments. Related to the leading noble of the court, Thomas Howard, Duke of Norfolk, Katherine was also a good catch. Henry reportedly "cast a fancy" to Katherine immediately upon her arrival. Katherine's step-grandmother instructed the girl how to behave with the King and bought her many new dresses to enhance her appearance. Just as he was courting Katherine, Henry tried to extricate himself from his loveless marriage.

Henry VIII's marriage to Anne of Cleves was annulled in July 1540 on the grounds of non-consummation. Anne suspected that Henry was in love with "that young girl Katherine", but there was little she could do to save her marriage.[4] On 28 July, Henry married Katherine at Oatlands Palace and signed the warrant of execution for Thomas Cromwell, his chief advisor who had arranged the King's fourth marriage. Several years later, Stephen Gardiner, Bishop of Winchester, would warn his fellow councillors how dangerous it was to "take a share in marriages of princes", citing Cromwell, who was ruined by the failed Cleves match.[5]

In September 1540, the Venetian ambassador Francesco Contarini reported that "the new Queen Katherine is said for certain to be pregnant".[6] The King's haste—he literally ended one marriage to start another—may be explained away by his belief that Katherine was expecting his child. There is enough evidence to support the notion that Henry VIII had sex with Katherine before their secret summer wedding. He often went by barge, accompanied by musicians, to meet Katherine in private. Her step-grandmother, Agnes Howard, knew very well that Katherine was not a virgin and instructed her "in what sort to entertain the King's Highness and how often".[7] The "how often" part may have referred to the number of sexual encounters Katherine was supposed to have with the King. Agnes also gave Katherine extra money for new clothes to enhance her appearance—after all, as soon as Henry VIII set his eyes on her she became an investment that could pay off in the future. Agnes Howard had good reasons to give Katherine advice because the girl was sexually experienced before she became Henry VIII's wife—something none of the Howards wanted the King to know.

Whether Katherine was truly pregnant in September 1540 is unknown, but on 31 December, the French ambassador Charles de Marillac reported that the Queen was "grosse"—stout.[8] This implied she was with child, and indeed, in April 1541 de Marillac continued to report about Katherine's pregnancy, writing "that this Queen is thought to be with child, which would be a very great joy to this King, who, it seems, believes it, and intends, if it be found true, to have her crowned at Whitsuntide".[9] De Marillac reported how the preparations for coronation were in full swing, which seems to prove the court was preparing for the coronation and then the christening of Katherine Howard's child. Ambassador Eustace Chapuys also reported that there was "some presumption that she [the Queen] was in the family way [pregnant]".[10] Unfortunately, nothing further was reported of this pregnancy. It seems that the young Queen was indeed pregnant but lost the child.

By November 1541, as he kneeled down in in the royal chapel at Hampton Court to receive the sacrament, Henry VIII felt that after four tempestuous marriages he was finally happy. He thought that "now in his old age" he had obtained "a jewel of womanhood".[11] Being married to the chronically ill King must have been trying for the young and vivacious Katherine, not to mention that she lived in constant fear of being replaced by another woman. By the time he married Katherine in 1540, Henry had the reputation of a husband who easily discarded his wives.

When Katherine Howard married Henry VIII, she had every reason to fear for her life, but it appeared that Henry was madly in love with her and had no intention of casting her aside. The King was "so amorous of her that he cannot treat her well enough and caresses her more than he did the others", reported Charles de Marillac.[12] Katherine reciprocated and played the part of a loving and obedient wife. There was "no other will but his", a motto she adopted upon becoming Queen and wore embroidered in gold thread around her sleeves. To keep up with his teenaged wife, Henry tamed his overeating and started physical exercise. Ambassador de Marillac observed that Henry "has taken a new rule of living: to rise between five and six in the morning, hear Mass at seven, and then ride until dinnertime, which is ten".[13]

On 1 November 1541, at the peak of his marital bliss, the King ordered his confessor to extoll Katherine and "to make prayer and give thanks with him for the good life he led and hoped to lead with her".[14] But this marital bliss was soon to come to an abrupt end.

During the progress in the summer of 1541, Thomas Cranmer, Archbishop of Canterbury, was approached by one John Lassells, who had something very important to communicate. Lassells's sister, Mary Hall, made an explosive revelation about the Queen's past. She used to serve as wet nurse to one of Agnes Howard's granddaughters and as the dowager duchess's chamberer afterwards. Lassells marvelled as to why his sister wouldn't apply for a job within the new Queen's household—as a former Howard employee, she would have been welcomed with open arms. But Mary said that the she felt "sorry for the Queen" because she was "light both in living and conditions", that is of loose morals and unchaste, and she would not become her servant.[15] Lassells teased his sister into revealing more, and Mary Hall told him everything she knew.

In the dowager duchess's household, there was one man in his early twenties named Francis Dereham who was sexually involved with Katherine Howard. Dereham, Mary asserted, "had lain in bed with her, in his doublet and hose, between the sheets one hundred nights". Girls in the household slept two to a bed, and one girl who slept with Katherine said that she would "lie no longer with her because she knew not what matrimony was". In other words, she had enough of listening to Katherine and Dereham making love. "Moreover", said Mary Hall, there was "one Mannock, a servant of the Duchess" who "knew a privy mark" on Katherine's body. The confession put a question mark over Katherine Howard's chastity. If she led such a life before her marriage, was it possible that she was unfaithful to the King now? It appeared to Cranmer that the Queen "was not a woman of such purity as was esteemed".[16]

Having such an explosive confession on his hands, the archbishop didn't know how to proceed. Knowing how much the King was in love with Katherine Howard, he dared not disturb the marital happiness, or worse, report false information. Being "much perplexed", Cranmer consulted Thomas Audley, Lord Chancellor, and Edward Seymour, Earl of Hertford, and they advised the archbishop to put the matter in writing as "he had not the heart to tell it by word of mouth". When the King picked up the letter left for him in the royal pew at Hampton Court on 2 November 1541, he reacted with disbelief and, "thinking the matter forged", summoned his closest advisers to deliberate.

William FitzWillliam, Earl of Southampton and Lord Privy Seal, was sent to examine John Lassells, "who stood to his declaration, saying he had made it only for the discharge of his duty".[17] After examining Lassells, FitzWilliam galloped off to Sussex to pay a visit to Mary Hall. In order to avoid the suspicion of Mary's husband, FitzWilliam went under the pretext of hunting in the nearby area. He reached Mary's house by 5 November. Mary described what had gone on between Katherine Howard and Henry Mannox, the music teacher who had taught Katherine (and presumably other girls as well) to play on the virginals. Mary saw that Mannox was romantically interested in Katherine and decided to chastise Mannox for his presumption, saying that Katherine came from a noble family "and if thou should marry her some of her blood would kill thee". Mannox ignored Mary's good advice and boasted: "I have had her by the cunt and she hath said to me that I shall have her maidenhead though it be painful to her, no doubting but I will be good to her thereafter."[18]

Just as FitzWilliam was conducting his investigations, Thomas Wriothesley was despatched to detain Francis Dereham on suspicion of piracy and examine Henry Mannox. When examining Mannox, Wriothesley was accompanied by Archbishop Cranmer. Mannox confessed that "he used to feel the secret parts" of Katherine's body "before Dereham was familiar with her". Mannox maintained that he fell in love with Katherine and she with him, but when the dowager duchess found them alone together one day, she "gave Mrs Katherine two or three blows, and charged them never to be alone together after". Then Mannox was replaced in Katherine's heart by Francis Dereham, of whom Mannox was bitterly jealous. He knew that Katherine and other ladies held late-night banquets in the maidens' chamber, lingering until two or three in the morning, feasting on fruit and wine and making love. Enraged, Mannox wrote the dowager duchess a letter wherein he informed her of the goings-on in the maidens' chamber and advising that if she "would rise half an hour after going to bed and visit the gentlewomen's chamber she would be displeased". The duchess "thereupon stormed with her women" and berated them for their recklessness. Katherine stole Mannox's letter and showed it to Dereham, who called Mannox a "knave". Mannox also implicated and named several people who could "speak of the misrule between Dereham and Mrs Katherine". Among them was Jane Bulmer, who sometimes shared Katherine's bed, Dorothy Dawby, the duchess's former chamberer, Katherine Tilney, Edward Waldegrave, Mary Lasselles (he didn't know that it was Mary's confession that spurred the investigation) and Malyn Tilney.[19]

Dereham, Mannox's rival for Katherine's affections, admitted freely that "he had known her carnally many times, both in his doublet and hose between the sheets and in naked bed", citing the names of three women who could confirm this.[20] Dereham was regarded by the council with great suspicion because Katherine Howard employed him in her royal household as a gentleman usher. Reporting the matter to William Paget, the King's ambassador in France, the councillors wrote collectively that the Queen's conduct before her marriage questioned whether she was faithful to the King since "she had already gotten this Dereham into her service and trained him upon occasions, as sending of errands and writing of letters when her secretary was out of the way, to come often into her privy chamber".[21]

If that wasn't enough, Katherine also employed Katherine Tilney, one of the girls who slept with her in the same bed in the dowager duchess's household and who was privy to her nocturnal meetings with Dereham. "What this pretended is easy to be conjectured", the councillors concluded, condemning the Queen's behaviour.[22] Katherine, it seems, employed Dereham out of obligation but had a sense that he was dangerous because of their past relationship. Dereham often boasted about their past romantic involvement, and the terrified Queen admonished him, warning to "take heed what words you speak" and giving him money twice, presumably to buy his silence.[23]

When he learned about Katherine Howard's past, Henry VIII's first reaction was disbelief. His initial order to investigate the matter further was motivated by a strong desire to clear his wife's name of slander and not to condemn her. Yet when John Lassells, Mary Hall, Francis Dereham and Henry Mannox all "agreed in one tale", thus confirming Katherine's youthful misdemeanours, the King was shocked. "On learning this, the King's heart was pierced with pensiveness, so that it was long before he could utter his sorrow", according to his councillors' collective letter to William Paget. When Henry finally composed himself and addressed his advisors, it was "with plenty of tears", which struck them as "strange" because many had never seen him cry before.[24]

The King left Hampton Court Palace secretly at night on Sunday, 5 November 1541. He would never see Katherine Howard again. It was typical of Henry VIII to distance himself from his disgraced wives without even saying good-bye. He did so ten years earlier, in the summer of 1531, when he sent a messenger to Katharine of Aragon ordering her to remove to Windsor. He would never see her again. It was similar with Anne Boleyn, whom the King saw for the last time on 1 May 1536 when they sat side by side under the canopy of estate watching the May Day joust. He left his seat so abruptly that "many men mused but most chiefly the Queen", who never saw her royal husband again.[25] Anne of Cleves, his fourth wife, was, ironically, the only wife he would see on occasion after their awkward breakup.

Katherine discovered the King's absence the next day, on 6 November, when a delegation of privy councillors headed by Archbishop Cranmer visited her in her private chambers and acquainted her with the charges lodged against her. The Queen had never received such a delegation in private, so when the men entered her chambers, with their golden chains of estate clanking, she must have felt that something had happened. She first caught a glimpse of Thomas Cranmer, Archbishop of Canterbury, who disclosed the matter to Henry VIII, leading the way. Right behind Cranmer stood Thomas Audley, Lord Chancellor, Stephen Gardiner, Bishop of Winchester and, last but not least, Katherine's uncle Thomas Howard, Duke of Norfolk.

The Queen received the delegation in her Presence Chamber at Hampton Court, sitting under the canopy of estate, flanked by her ladies-in-waiting. When she was informed that her past romantic involvement with Francis Dereham had been discovered, she remained composed and "constantly denied it".[26] Faced with the Queen's resistance, Cranmer decided to return to talk to her in private, without the intimidating presence of Audley, Gardiner and Norfolk. Eustace Chapuys, the imperial ambassador who came to England in 1529 and who witnessed all of the King's previous marriages and their disintegration, wrote: "After the King had left, the Archbishop of Canterbury entered the Queen's chamber two or three times to interrogate and admonish her, as is supposed, on the part of the Council, but he did not make much out."[27] Chapuys's reports indicate that the Queen was anguished and restless and didn't start to cooperate at once. Cranmer, whose report of what transpired is still extant, confirmed that Katherine was in a deeply fragile mental state.

"I found her in such lamentation and heaviness, as I never saw no creature", the archbishop wrote to the King on the evening of 6 November. Between Cranmer's visits, Katherine agonised over her fate. The archbishop empathised with the Queen, writing to Henry that "it would have pitied any man's heart in the world to have looked upon her". Katherine continued in "vehement rage" and was too disturbed to answer the archbishop's questions, and this was the reason why Cranmer visited her several times, giving her an opportunity to calm down and gather her thoughts.[28] In his letter to the King, Cranmer wrote about Katherine's "vehement rage", "estrame braids", "great pang", "frenzy" and uncontrollable crying—all of this indicates that she suffered a nervous breakdown or experienced panic attacks. When the archbishop "declared your grace's mercy extended to her", Katherine "held up her hands and gave most humble thanks unto your majesty, who had showed unto her more grace and mercy than she herself thought meet to sue for or could have hoped of; and then, for a time, she began to be more temperate and quiet, saving that she still sobbed and wept; but after a little pausing she suddenly fell into a new rage, much worse than she was before". Cranmer's further description of Katherine's behaviour confirms that she was very anxious and hysterical:

"When I do see her in any such extreme braids, I do travail with her to know the cause, and then, as much as I can, I do labour to take away, or at the least to mitigate the cause; and so I did at that time. I told her there was some new fantasy come into her head, which I desired her to open unto me; and after a certain time, when she had recovered herself that she might speak, she cried and said: 'Alas, my lord, that I am alive! The fear of death grieved me not so much before, as doth now the remembrance of the

King's goodness: for when I remember how gracious and loving a prince I had, I cannot but sorrow; but this sudden mercy, and more than I could have looked for, showed unto me, so unworthy, at this time, maketh mine offences to appear before mine eyes much more heinous than they did before: and the more I consider the greatness of his mercy, the more I do sorrow in my heart that I should so misorder myself against his majesty.' And for anything that I could say unto her, she continued in a great pang a long while; but after that she began something to remit her rage and come to herself, she was meetly well until night, and I had very good communication with her, and, as I thought, had brought her unto a great quietness."

It appeared to Cranmer that he calmed the Queen, but "about six of the clock, she fell into another like pang, but not so outrageous as the first was".[29] This was because she remembered that Thomas Heneage, a gentleman of the King's Privy Chamber, usually came with a message from Henry at this hour; this time there was no message. French ambassador Charles de Marillac confirmed Cranmer's report, writing that Katherine refused to "drink or eat and weeps and cries like a madwoman, so that they must take away things by which she might hasten her death."[30]

In any case, Cranmer managed to assure Katherine of Henry's goodwill so that she would confess more about her relationship with Francis Dereham. It was Cranmer's goal to make the Queen confess that she and Dereham had entered into a pre-contract. Dereham claimed that he and Katherine had agreed to marry. Such a promise, if made in front of witnesses and consummated afterwards, was as binding as marriage before a priest. If Katherine and Dereham were pre-contracted to each other, then Katherine's marriage to the King was invalid. This could potentially save the Queen from the executioner's blade, but Katherine steadfastly denied that any pre-contract ever existed.

Yet Cranmer pursued the pre-contract issue and asked the Queen if she and Dereham called each other husband and wife, to which Katherine replied as follows:

"Examined whether I called him husband, and he me wife. I do answer, that there was communication in the house that we two should marry together; and some of his enemies had envy thereat, wherefore, he desired me to give him leave to call me wife, and that I would call him husband. And I said I was content. And so after that, commonly he called me wife, and many times I called him husband. And he used many times to kiss me, and so he did to many others in the house. And, I suppose, that this be true, that at one time when he kissed me very often, some said that were present, 'They trowed that he would never have kissed me enough'. Whereunto he answered, 'Who should let [hinder] him to kiss his own wife?' Then said one of them, 'I trowe this matter will come to pass as the common saying is'. 'What is that', quoth he. 'Marry', said the other, 'that Mr Dereham shall have Mrs Katherine Howard'. 'By St John' said Dereham, 'you may guess twice, and guess worse'. But that I should wink upon him, and say secretly, 'What if this should come to my Lady's ear?' I suppose verily there was no such thing."

Cranmer pursued the subject of the consummation of their union. Had she and Dereham ever made love to each other? This time Katherine's reply tallied with Dereham's earlier confession:

"As for carnal knowledge, I confess as I did before, that divers times he hath lay with me, sometimes in his doublet and hose, and two or three times naked: But not so naked that he had nothing upon him, for he had always at the least had his doublet, and as I do think, his hose also, but I mean naked when his hose were put down."

Was it true, Cranmer continued, that Dereham brought in fruit and wine to the maidens' chamber? Indeed, that was true: "And divers times he would bring wine, strawberries, apples, and other things to make good cheer, after my Lady was gone to bed." Mary Hall had testified that Katherine often stole the keys from Agnes Howard and that she was the person who was responsible for organising the late-night banquets, but Katherine said that this was "utterly untrue", adding:

"Nor I never did steal the keys myself, nor desired any person to steal them, to that intent and purpose to let Dereham in, but for many other causes the doors have been opened, sometimes overnight, and sometimes early in the morning, as well at the request of me, as of other."

Cranmer also wanted to know when and how Katherine and Dereham broke off the relationship. Katherine remembered that when she told Dereham that she was soon to leave for court, he replied that "if I were gone, he would not tarry long in the house". Katherine, somewhat coldly, said that "he may do as he list [wished]". Dereham painted a different picture at their farewell—Katherine, with tears streaming down her cheeks, said that their parting grieved her. Katherine denied this. "For all that he knew me, and kept my company, knew how glad and desirous I was to come to the court", she confessed.[31] It seems that Dereham was still in love with Katherine when he received the news that she was the King's new love interest. "I could be sure [married] to Mistress Katherine, and I would; but I dare not", he boasted to his friend. "The King begynethe to love her; but, and he were dead, I am sure I might marry her".[32]

When Cranmer was about to leave after this final interview, Katherine "began to excuse and to temper those things which she had spoken unto me, and set her hand thereunto". He was referring to the confession she had just signed. Perhaps the Queen believed she had said too much about her involvement with Dereham because it sounded as if she had sex with him of her own free will. Now, when the archbishop was heading towards the door, Katherine panicked, stopped him and said that "all that Dereham did unto her was of his importune forcement, and, in a manner, violence, rather than of her free consent and will".[33] This confession didn't make it into the official report of the examination of the Queen, but Cranmer included it in his letter to Henry VIII written later that night and allowed Katherine to write to the King.

Writing to the King, Katherine represented herself as a frail woman abused by men who took advantage of her youth:

"First, at the flattering and fair persuasions of Mannox, being but a young girl, suffered him at sundry times to handle and touch the secret parts of my body which neither became me with honesty to permit nor him to require . . . Also Francis Dereham by many persuasions procured me to his vicious purpose and obtained first to lye upon my bed with his doublet and hose and after within the bed and finally he lay with me naked and used me in such sort as a man doth his wife many and sundry times but how often I know not, and our company ended almost a year before the King's Majesty was married to my Lady Anne of Cleves and continued not past on quarter of a year or little above."[34]

In her comment to Cranmer and letter to Henry, Katherine was implying that she was raped by Dereham, but was it true? In recent years it became popular to depict Katherine as a victim of sexual abuse, but it appears that she was not raped. If Dereham raped her, why didn't Katherine say so during the long hours of initial interrogation? In determining whether or not rape took place, it's helpful to examine the interrogations of people who knew Katherine and Dereham and witnessed what went on between them.

Mary Hall, whose confession to her brother sparked the investigation into Katherine's conduct, said that there was "such puffing and blowing" between Katherine and Dereham at night that Alice Wilkes, who shared a bed with Katherine, said that she would not sleep with her again because "she knew not what matrimony meant". There was no mention of struggle or violence, just "puffing and blowing", indicative of consensual sex.[35] Also, Mary was under the impression that Katherine and Dereham were "far in love together" because she saw them once "kiss after a wonderful manner for they would kiss and hang by the beaks together an [as though] they were two sparrows".[36]

Mary was not the only one who believed Dereham and Katherine were in love. Dereham's friend Robert Damport saw the two "kiss often and lie together upon the bed". This took place "in the duchess's bedchamber openly in the sight of diverse people many times". Again, no violence or struggle, just two young lovers being affectionate with each other. One Margaret Benet looked through a keyhole and "saw Dereham pluck up Katherine's clothes above her navel". Dereham also took Katherine "to the jakes", or privies, to have sex with her there.[37]

Margaret Benet also eavesdropped on the conversations between Katherine and Dereham and overheard how Dereham told Katherine that "although he used the company of [had sex with] a woman hundred times yet he would get no child except he listed [wished]". Katherine replied in similar vein, saying that "a woman might meddle [have sex] with a man and yet conceive no child unless she would [wanted] for herself".[38] The couple may have been speaking about contraception and ways to prevent unwanted pregnancy, but it's also possible that they were referring to the belief that a woman had to enjoy sex if she wanted to conceive a child.

Andrew Maunsey, servant of the dowager duchess, was examined and said that:

"[W]hen he was in household with the duchess he thrice saw the Queen, then Mrs Katherine Howard, lie in her bed and one Durand [Dereham], a gentleman then in the house, lie suspiciously on the bed in his doublet and hose. Katherine Tilney lay in the bed at the time and can tell more. A laundry woman named Besse can also speak of this. It was twelve months before the Queen came to court."[39]

Maunsey saw Dereham lying on Katherine's bed dressed only in his doublet and hose, as Dereham and Katherine often said happened. Maunsey mentioned no struggle or violence. Katherine Tilney, Katherine's former bedfellow and friend whom the Queen employed as chamberer in her royal household, imparted more or less the same information. It was her understanding that Katherine and Dereham were in love and pursued their relationship in secret so as not to displease the dowager duchess, who nevertheless knew that "there was love between them".[40] The duchess would often laughingly say when looking for Dereham that "I am sure he is sleeping in the gentlewomen's chamber" and found him there lying upon one bed or another.[41] It was well-known in Agnes Howard's household that Dereham was in love with Katherine and that she reciprocated his feelings. Yet when the opportunity came to leave the household and join the court, Katherine didn't hesitate; it appears she fell out of love with Dereham, but he still hoped to win her hand in marriage.

Dereham appears to have been an arrogant, overconfident young man who was inclined to bullying and bravado. At the same time, he appears to have been a charming smooth talker. Agnes Howard thought so highly of him that she gave him a shirt that belonged to her late son Lord Thomas Howard.

When Dereham learned that Katherine had become Queen, he decided to use the connection between them to advance himself socially. Katherine employed him, apparently after Agnes Howard's solicitation, as was customary in an age when loyalty to family and friends was important. At court, Dereham boasted several times about his friendship with Katherine, oblivious to the fact that such bragging could put them both in great danger. Robert Davenport, Dereham's friend from the dowager duchess's household, mentioned that Dereham told him that "many despised him" since he came to court "because the Queen favoured him". Dereham had a habit of staying at the table with members of the Queen's council when lower servants left. As a mere usher, Dereham was not entitled to dine with the Queen's council, and when one Mr Johns, the Queen's gentleman usher and Dereham's colleague, sent him a messenger with admonitions, Dereham retorted: "Go to Mr Johns, and tell him I was of the Queen's council before he knew her and shall be when she hath forgotten him." Dereham's boasts frightened Katherine enough to warn him to "take heed what words you speak" and give him money on two recorded instances, likely to buy his silence.[42]

Katherine was right to fear Dereham's big mouth. Over the course of his interrogation, Dereham learned, to his dismay, that it was presumed that he and the Queen continued their relationship. Dereham, "to show his innocence since the marriage, said that Culpeper had succeeded him in the Queen's affections".[43]

Dereham's mention of Thomas Culpeper, gentleman of the King's Privy Chamber, marked a turning point in the investigation. So far, the Queen had been accused of unchaste life before her marriage to Henry VIII and hiding a possible pre-contract with Francis Dereham. Now it appeared that she was romantically involved with a gentleman at court during her marriage to the King. If this proved to have been true, the Queen faced death on charges of adultery.

Francis Dereham's mention of Thomas Culpeper shifted the councillors' attention from Katherine Howard's adolescence to her present circumstances. During her interrogation on 6 November, the Queen herself mentioned Culpeper. She recalled that when Dereham came to court he asked her if "I should be married to Mr Culpeper, for so he said he heard reported". "Why should you trouble me therewith, for you know I will not have you", Katherine snapped, adding: "if you heard such report, you heard more than I do know".[44] When Katherine started her career at court, she met and apparently fell in love with Thomas Culpeper. There was talk of the two marrying, but nothing came of it, and Culpeper moved on to another conquest. The matter was forgotten when Katherine caught the King's eye. But the young Queen could or would not forget about Culpeper.

Katherine's panicked outbursts and "frenzy" described by Archbishop Cranmer in a letter to the King on 6 November 1541 gain significance in light of her involvement with Culpeper. It was not her past with Francis Dereham that worried Katherine so much that she feared death, it was her relationship with Thomas Culpeper that she was afraid would be her downfall. This is confirmed by Jane Boleyn, Viscountess Rochford, Katherine's closest lady-in-waiting, who testified that "since her trouble the Queen has daily asked for Culpeper, saying that if that matter came not out she feared not."[45] Lady Rochford, as she was commonly known at court, was in a position to know much about Katherine's infatuation with Culpeper, for she acted as their go-between, arranging meetings, carrying gifts and messages, and making sure the Queen was as discreet as possible.

Thomas Culpeper was a young man brought up at court who served as gentleman of the King's Privy Chamber and slept in a pallet bed in the royal bedchamber. Highly favoured by the King, two years earlier Culpeper managed to get away with murder and brutal rape.[46] At court, Culpeper cut a glamorous figure and impressed ladies with his charisma, charm and impeccable manners. Unmarried, he freely indulged in the pleasures of the flesh, seducing at least three women: Anne Herbert, Countess of Pembroke, Dorothy Bray and Bessie Harvey.

The Queen renewed her interest in Culpeper during Easter of 1541 and pursued their relationship throughout the summer progress in the north. Whatever was happening between them, Katherine knew it could damage her reputation, hence her frantic behaviour with the Archbishop of Canterbury.

Confined to her chambers with Lady Rochford in attendance, Katherine was wondering how much the Privy Council knew about her and Culpeper. On the morning of 12 November, Lady Rochford told the Queen to "hold her own for Culpeper was merry at hawking yesterday". This implied that his life went on as usual and that he wasn't detained. Katherine, somewhat ungraciously, replied that she marvelled that Lady Rochford was not examined by the council. She admonished her, saying, "it would [get] out, what hold your own I warrant [assure] you, be you afraid".[47] Lady Rochford feared that the Queen would break under strain and inform the council about her secret trysts with Culpeper, and she warned Katherine not to say anything. "They would speak fair words to you and use all ways with you but and if you confess, you would undo yourself and others". She also assured the Queen that she would never confess anything even if "I was torn with wild horses".[48]

Lady Rochford's optimism was misplaced, however, since Culpeper was arrested shortly after he returned from his merry session of hawking. During the interrogation, he admitted that he had several private meetings with the Queen, but they were not sexual in nature. He said that the Queen started favouring him during Easter of 1541 when she gave him a velvet cap decorated with a brooch and ordered him to tuck it beneath his cloak so that nobody would see it. This in itself gives an interesting insight into their relationship—Katherine, far from the silly girl she is so often said to have been, warned Culpeper not to show the cap to anyone. This implies that she wanted to be careful in her dealings with Culpeper and keep their relationship secret.

The conversations reported by Culpeper were laced with sexual innuendo. When, during one of their secretive meetings late at night, Katherine teased Culpeper that she could "bring you into as good a trade as Bray hath my Lord Parr in", Culpeper replied that he thought the Queen was "no such woman as Bray". Katherine's bold reply highlights the fact that she didn't hide her past from Culpeper: "Well, if I had tarried still in the maidens' chamber I would have tried you."[49] Her words make it clear that Katherine hadn't been raped in the maidens' chamber by Francis Dereham; why would she brag about "trying" Culpeper there if she was a victim of sexual abuse? In fact, these words imply that Katherine willingly participated in sex. It appears that Katherine engaged in sexual activities with delight and was implying to Culpeper that she would have had sex with him had she been still a simple Katherine Howard and not Queen Katherine.

Careful examination of the original interrogations of Thomas Culpeper and Katherine Howard show that their confessions tally, sometimes alarmingly closely. Culpeper gave detailed descriptions of "many stolen interviews with the Queen" at Greenwich, Lincoln, Pontefract and York, claiming that "Lady Rochford contrived these interviews". Thomas Culpeper claimed that although he "had intended to do ill with the Queen", i.e. to have sex with her, the only naked part of her body he kissed was her hand. Katherine, interrogated on 12 November, corroborated his testimony, swearing upon oath that Culpeper never "touched any bare of her but her hand". The way they couched their confessions strongly implies that they talked about what to say in case their relationship was discovered. It's strange indeed that they would both use the exact same wording when denying that sex took place between them. What's even more suspicious is that both portrayed themselves as innocent parties, manipulated by the Queen's closest lady-in-waiting, Jane Boleyn. Culpeper, examined before the Queen, was first to point an accusatory finger at Jane, saying that "Lady Rochford contrived these interviews". Katherine, examined on 12 November, corroborated his statement but in more detail:

"The Queen said that my Lady Rochford had sundry times made instance [solicitation] to her to speak with Culpeper declaring him to bear her goodwill and favour, whereupon she did at the last grant he should speak with her, my Lady of Rochford affirming that he desired nothing else but to speak with her and that she durst swear upon a book he meant nothing but honesty."

Katherine then went on to detail when and where she met with Culpeper during progress:

"And so he spoke with her in a little gallery at the stairs head at Lincoln when it was late in the night about ten or eleven of the clock, an hour and more, another time in her bedchamber at Pontefract and another time in my Lady of Rochford's chamber at York."

It wasn't easy for the two to meet in private, so somebody had to look for suitable places that ensured a maximum degree of privacy. In Katherine's version, that somebody was Lady Rochford, who "would at every lodging search the back doors and tell her of them if there were any, unasked; and since the progress she [Jane] told her [Katherine] that when she came to Greenwich she knew an old kitchen wherein she might well speak with him". Culpeper, on the other hand, thought that it was the Queen who would "in every house seek for the back doors and back stairs herself". Katherine went further and portrayed herself as a victim of Lady Rochford's manipulations, saying that "she would ever [always] say to my Lady Rochford when she moved [plead with] her for him, 'alas madam this would be spied one day and then we be all undone', whereunto my Lady Rochford would say 'fear not madam let me alone I warrant [assure] you'. One day, Katherine recalled, when Lady Rochford spoke highly of Culpeper, the Queen admonished her, saying: "Alas madam will this never have an end. I pray you, bid him desire no more to trouble me or send to me." When Lady Rochford informed Culpeper of the Queen's words, he would beseech the Queen "to send him no such word for he would take no such answer" and still sent a messenger to her, for which the Queen "called him little sweet fool". The Queen also said that Lady Rochford told her that another young man at court called Paston bore her favour, but nothing came of it.

Lest someone would ask why she never stood up to her manipulative servant, Katherine confessed that she warned Lady Rochford to "trouble her no more with such light matters" to which Jane replied, "yet must you give men leave to look for they will look upon you".[50] The picture Katherine painted was that of a bullied young woman who was manipulated and forced by her lady-in-waiting to enter into a relationship with a handsome courtier.[51] Yet a letter Katherine wrote to Culpeper when he fell sick questions the veracity of her own version of events. The letter bears no date but is signed by the Queen:

"Master Culpeper,

I heartily recommend me unto you, praying you to send me word how that you do. It was showed me that you was sick, the which thing troubled me very much till such time that I hear from you praying you to send me word how that you do, for I never longed so much for a thing as I do to see you and to speak with you, the which I trust shall be shortly now. That which doth comfort me very much when I think of it, and when I think again that you shall depart from me again it makes my heart die to think what fortune I have that I cannot be always in your company. It my trust is always in you that you will be as you have promised me, and in that hope I trust upon still, praying you that you will come when my Lady Rochford is here for then I shall be best at leisure to be at your commandment, thanking you for that you have promised me to be so good unto that poor fellow my man which is one of the griefs that I do feel to depart from him for then I do know no one that I dare trust to send to you, and therefore I pray you take him to be with you that I may sometime hear from you one thing. I pray you to give me a horse for my man for I had much ado to get one and therefore I pray send me one by him and in so doing I am as I said afore, and thus I take my leave of you, trusting to see you shortly again and I would you was with me now that you might see what pain I take in writing to you.

Yours as long as life endures,

Katheryn.

One thing I had forgotten and that is to instruct my man to tarry here with me still for he says whatsomever you bid him he will do it."[52]

The letter was found among Culpeper's things and deemed useful or damning enough to be carefully examined and used as evidence against the Queen. Years later a story about how the Queen sent Culpeper a love letter was still circulating at court and abroad.[53] Far from a manipulated and bullied woman, the letter depicts Katherine as in love with Culpeper, for it made her "heart die to think what fortune I have that I cannot be always in your company". Her trust, Katherine wrote, "is always in you", and she longed to see and speak to him again. Culpeper fondly preserved the letter and later said that the Queen "was actually dying of love for his person", not an unreasonable supposition based on the letter's content.

The Queen's other ladies-in-waiting who were interrogated remembered Katherine as the driving force behind the secret trysts with Culpeper. Katherine Tilney, the Queen's chamberer and bedfellow from Norfolk House, confessed that at Lincoln "the Queen went two nights to Lady Rochford's chamber, which was up a little pair of stairs by the Queen's chamber". Tilney took another chamberer with her, Margaret Morton, to check what was going on, but both were "sent back". It was late at night and Tilney went to bed, but Mistress Morton, ever so curious, went to Lady Rochford's chamber again to see what was happening but was unable to learn anything. It was two o'clock in the morning, and Katherine Tilney asked Morton, "Jesus, is not the Queen abed yet?" to which Morton replied, "Yes, even now". Another chamberer, Mistress Lufkin, went to check on the Queen, and when she knocked, Lady Rochford, freshly woken up, opened the door.

The Queen apparently learned of her nosy servants' endeavours to find out where she was at night and conceived a strong dislike for Morton and Lufkin. "At Pontefract the Queen was angry with Mrs Lufkin and me and threatened to put us away", i.e. dismiss them, Morton confessed. If that happened, Morton believed that the Queen would fill the vacancies with servants recommended by Lady Rochford. This implies that Morton didn't like Lady Rochford very much. She was observant enough to see that something sinister was happening on progress and opined that "my lady of Rochford was the principal occasion of her [the Queen's] folly". She based her observation on what was happening at Pontefract Castle, where the Queen spent every night in one chamber with Lady Rochford, bolting the doors from within. It seems that after Lincoln, the Queen wanted to make sure that none of her chamberers would come knocking at her door, or if they did, they wouldn't be able to come in. The activities within Katherine's chambers were very close to being discovered at Pontefract since the King sent his groom of the stool, Anthony Denny, to fetch Katherine to him, but the door was bolted, and he couldn't come in.

Whenever Katherine talked with Culpeper, Lady Rochford would "many times, being ever by, sit somewhat far off or turn her back". In Katherine's view, this was unacceptable because Lady Rochford was supposed to be her chaperone, so she snapped at her, saying, "For God's sake madam even near us". This may have been true as Lady Rochford confessed that during Katherine's meetings with Culpeper she either heard or saw nothing because "the Queen was at the other end of the room and Culpeper on the stairs, ready to slip down". "At Lincoln, when the Queen was with Culpeper", Jane said she "was asleep until the

Queen called her to answer Lufkin". Although she tried to convince the councillors who interrogated her that she wasn't privy to what was happening between the Queen and Culpeper, Jane said she believed that the couple had sex.

Whatever happened between Katherine Howard and Thomas Culpeper was, however, not important to the councillors who interrogated them. The fact that Katherine, a married woman, was having late-night meetings with another man was damning enough. Francis Dereham and Thomas Culpeper were tried for treason at Guildhall on 1 December 1541 "for high treason against the King's Majesty in misdemeanour with the Queen".[54] Chronicler Edward Hall recorded:

"At this time the Queen late before married to the King called Queen Katherine, was accused to the King of dissolute living, before her marriage, with Francis Dereham, and that was not secretly, but many knew it. And since her marriage, she was vehemently suspected with Thomas Culpeper, which was brought to her Chamber at Lincoln, in August last, in the Progress time, by the Lady of Rochford, and were there together alone, from eleven of the clock at night, till four of the clock in the morning, and to him she gave a chain, and a rich cap."[55]

Secret meetings of Katherine and Culpeper were indicative of the couple's intentions to have sex, whereas Dereham's joining the Queen's household was seen as damning evidence that he wanted to renew his romantic relationship with her. Both men were sentenced to be "drawn, hanged and quartered".[56] Both Dereham and Culpeper served at court, so the Privy Council raised the possibility of their sentences being commuted to the more merciful beheading with an axe.

The King, who took an active part in the case by reading and amending interrogatories and having regular briefings, would not budge. "As to the remission of the extremity of Dereham's judgment, the King thinks he has deserved no such mercy".[57] Thomas Culpeper's sentence was commuted, and he was given the privilege of dying before Dereham. On 10 December 1541, Culpeper exhorted the people to pray for him, kneeled by the gallows "and had his head stricken off", presumably in one clean cut. Dereham suffered the full horror of being "hanged, dismembered, disembowelled, beheaded and quartered".[58] Their heads were put on display on London Bridge. Nothing remained of Dereham's maimed body, whereas Culpeper's headless corpse was buried at the Church of the Holy Sepulchre at Newgate.

When Katherine Howard was rowed from Syon Abbey to the Tower on 10 February 1542, the stark reality hit her hard as she passed by the decapitated heads of Thomas Culpeper and Francis Dereham. At that moment, she realised there was no hope for her. When informed about her impending execution, the young woman asked that a wooden block should be brought to her chamber so that she could practice how to put her head on it. It was a reasonable request: Katherine had certainly heard that an inexperienced executioner could hack her head and shoulders to pieces and painfully injure her before striking the final blow, and she wanted to be prepared.

The Queen's lady-in-waiting, "that bawd, Lady Rochford", as her indictment condemned her, apparently underwent some form of mental breakdown during her arrest. English law prohibited execution if the accused had been declared insane. The King allowed Lady Rochford to recuperate in the house of the Lord Admiral, where she was cared for by his wife, Anne Russell. The imperial ambassador heard that Lady Rochford had regained her senses when she learned that she would die regardless of whether she was insane or not. The King was so eager to send her to the scaffold "as an example and warning to others" that he had passed a special law allowing him to execute an insane person.[59]

On the crisp wintry morning of 13 February 1542, Katherine Howard made her way to the wooden scaffold erected on the spot where, six years earlier, her cousin Anne Boleyn had been executed for adultery. The young Queen was "so weak that she could hardly speak" and kept her speech brief.[60] When the executioner performed his task, Lady Rochford approached the scaffold and had to put her head down on the wooden block where her royal mistress had lost her life only minutes before. An eyewitness recorded that both Katherine Howard and Jane Boleyn "made the most godly and Christians' end that ever was heard tell of (I think) since the world's creation".[61] They confessed their guilt and asked the gathered crowd to pray for Henry VIII's wealth and prosperity.

NOTES

[1] For a detailed discussion of Katherine Howard's date of birth see Gareth Russell, *Young and Damned and Fair*, pp. 14-16.
[2] M.A. Sharp Hume, *Chronicle of King Henry VIII of England*, p. 75.
[3] *Ibid.* See also *Letters and Papers, Foreign and Domestic,* Volume 16, n. 12, for de Marillac's comment.
[4] Hastings Robinson, *Original Letters*, Volume 1, p. 205.

[5] John Schofield, *The Rise and Fall of Thomas Cromwell*, p. 409.
[6] *Calendar of State Papers Relating To English Affairs in the Archives of Venice*, Volume 5, n. 226.
[7] *Letters and Papers, Foreign and Domestic, Henry VIII*, Volume 16, n. 1409, 3.
[8] Ibid., n. 373.
[9] Ibid., n. 712.
[10] *Calendar of State Papers, Spain*, Volume 6 Part 1, n. 204.
[11] *Letters and Papers, Foreign and Domestic, Henry VIII*, Volume 16, n. 1334.
[12] Ibid., n. 12.
[13] Ibid., n. 311.
[14] Ibid., n. 1334.
[15] Ibid., n. 1320.
[16] Ibid., 1334.
[17] Ibid.
[18] Gareth Russell, *Young and Damned and Fair*, pp. 55-56.
[19] *Letters and Papers, Foreign and Domestic, Henry VIII*, Volume 16, n. 1321.
[20] Ibid., n. 1321.
[21] Ibid.
[22] Ibid.
[23] Ibid., n. 1339.
[24] Ibid., n. 1334.
[25] Edward Hall, *Hall's Chronicle*, p. 876.
[26] *Letters and Papers, Foreign and Domestic, Henry VIII*, Volume 16, n. 1334.
[27] Ibid., n. 1328.
[28] *Miscellaneous Writings and Letters of Thomas Cranmer*, p. 406.
[29] Ibid.
[30] *Letters and Papers, Foreign and Domestic*, Henry VIII, Volume 16, n. 1342.
[31] Gilbert Burnet, *The History of the Reformation of the Church of England*, pp. 171-173.
[32] *State Papers*, Volume 1, p. 698.
[33] *Miscellaneous Writings and Letters of Thomas Cranmer*, p. 409.
[34] *Calendar of the Manuscripts of the Marquis of Bath*, pp. 8-9.
[35] TNA SP1/167, fols. 138, 140.
[36] TNA SP 1/167/128-31
[37] TNA SP 1/167/162
[38] Ibid.

[39] *Letters and Papers, Foreign and Domestic, Henry VIII,* Volume 16, n. 1348.
[40] Ibid., n. 1385.
[41] Ibid., n. 1416.
[42] Ibid., n. 1339.
[43] Ibid., n. 1366.
[44] Gilbert Burnet, *The History of the Reformation of the Church*, p. 173.
[45] Ibid., n. 1339.
[46] Gareth Russell, *Young and Damned and Fair*, p. 247.
[47] *Calendar of the Manuscripts of the Marquis of Bath*, p. 10.
[48] Ibid.
[49] *Letters and Papers, Foreign and Domestic, Henry VIII,* Volume 16, n. 1339.
[50] TNA SP 1/167/ fols. 159-160.
[51] In *Wicked Women of Tudor England*, Retha M. Warnicke proposed that "Culpeper was bribing Lady Rochford to obtain access to the queen and then blackmailing Katherine to force her to present him with gifts and to meet with him". (p. 76).
[52] TNA SP 1/167/14: The undated letter from Katherine Howard to Thomas Culpeper.
[53] *Chronicle of King Henry VIII of England*, pp. 82-87.
[54] Charles Wriothesley, *A Chronicle of England During the Reigns of the Tudors, from A.D. 1485 to 155*, p. 131-132.
[55] Edward Hall, *Hall's Chronicle*, p. 842.
[56] Charles Wriothesley, op.cit.
[57] *Letters and Papers, Foreign and Domestic, Henry VIII,* Volume 16, n. 1425.
[58] Charles Wriothesley, op.cit.
[59] *Calendar of State Papers, Spain,* Volume 6 Part 1, n. 209.
[60] *Letters and Papers, Foreign and Domestic, Henry VIII,* Volume 17, n. 100.
[61] Ibid., n. 106.

CHAPTER 16: "DELIVERED OF A FAIR BOY"

Just as the investigation into Katherine Howard's behaviour was carried out in November of 1541, Henry VIII was informed that his ex-wife, Anne of Cleves, "was delivered of a fair boy".[1] Rumour had it that Anne had given birth in October to a son fathered by the King. The rumour was told to Richard Taverner, one of the four Clerks of the Royal Signet, "both by his mother-in-law, Lambert's wife, the goldsmith, and by Taverner's own wife, who said she heard it of Lilgrave's wife, and Lambert's wife heard it, also, of the old Lady Carewe. Taverner kept it [to himself], but they with others have made it common matter of talk. Taverner never revealed it till Sunday night [4 December], when he told it to Dr Cox".[2]

The rumour wasn't dismissed outright because it appears to have originated in the royal household, and this sole fact gave it a semblance of probability. Richard Taverner enjoyed a long and prosperous career at Henry VIII's court, translating the Bible known as *The Most Sacred Bible* in 1539. An Oxford graduate, he started his career under the auspices of Cardinal Wolsey, joining Thomas

Cromwell's household after the cardinal's fall from grace. Taverner's wife was Margaret, daughter of Walter Lambert of Chertsey and Margaret Gainsford. The Lilgraves served as Anne of Cleves's embroiderers, whereas the "old Lady Carew" may have been the mother of Wymond Carew, the disgruntled receiver in Anne of Cleves's household.[3]

According to this rumour, Anne of Cleves's son was conceived during Anne's visit to Hampton Court in December 1540. Anne had been treated with respect, and the King inviting her to Christmas festivities bred rumours that the two might reconcile. Two ambassadors, French Charles de Marillac and imperial Eustace Chapuys, recorded the existence of such "bruits", with Chapuys attributing them to the fact that Katherine Howard, Henry's beloved young wife, was barren.[4] On 4 December, Anne of Cleves's servant Jane Ratsey had been examined about her utterances regarding the King's marriage to Anne. Ratsey apparently talked with her colleague, Katherine Bassett, about recent events at court. She mused about Katherine Howard's arrest: "What if God worketh this work to make the lady Anne of Cleves Queen again?" In her own defence, Ratsey said that it was only "an idle saying suggested by Bassett's praising the Lady Anne and dispraising the Queen that now is". But that was not all. Ratsey also mused about the King's marital status: "What a man is the King! How many wives will he have?" She said it "upon the sudden tidings declared to her by Bassett, when she was sorry for the change and knew not so much as she knows now". In the end, Jane Ratsey said that she believed that the divorce between Henry VIII and Anne of Cleves was "good", i.e. binding, and that she didn't mean anything treasonous by what she said.[5]

On 8 December 1541, Richard Taverner and Frances Lilgrave were arrested. Lilgrave was said to have "slandered the lady Anne of Cleves, and therein the King also" and "could bring no author of her slander". Taverner, on the other hand, was accused of "concealing the said slander and not reporting it himself".[6] On 11 December, Eustace Chapuys reported:

"Two honest citizens were imprisoned three days ago for having said, since the Queen's misbehaviour was published, that the whole thing seemed a judgment of God, for the lady of Cleves was really the King's wife, and that though the rumour had been purposely spread that the King had had no connection with her, the contrary might be asserted, as she was known to have gone away from

London in the family way, and had been confined last summer—a rumour which has been widely circulated."[7]

Henry VIII took rumours of Anne of Cleves's secret pregnancy and confinement seriously:

"His Majesty thinketh it requisite to have it groundly examined and further ordered by your discretions, as the manner of the case requireth, to inquire diligently whether the said Lady Anne of Cleves hath indeed had any child or no, as it is bruited, for his Majesty hath been informed that it is so indeed, in which part his Majesty imputeth a great default in her officers for not advising [informing] his Highness thereof if it be true."[8]

On 6 December, Jane Ratsey was re-examined, this time about what she knew about Anne of Cleves's secret pregnancy and confinement.[9] Three days later Mrs Ratsey was committed to the custody of Sir Thomas Audley, Lord Chancellor, and officers of Anne of Cleves's household were summoned, as was Dorothy Wingfield, one of the women of Anne's Privy Chamber.[10] Mrs Ratsey was very "sorrowful" about her words concerning the King and begged for his forgiveness. Henry, moved by her "sorrowfulness", decided to forgive her on understanding that her words didn't proceed from malice. On 10 December, she was set at liberty.[11]

On 30 December, Frances Lilgrave finally admitted to "having slandered the Lady Anne and touched also the King's person, she affirming to have heard the report of others, whom she refused to name".[12] She and Richard Taverner were committed to the Tower but were both later released.[13]

Anne of Cleves was aware that she was very popular among the English people. Charles de Marillac reported on the on-going rumours that Henry VIII would remarry her, saying that Anne "has conducted herself wisely in her affliction, and is more beautiful than she was, and more regretted and commiserated than Queen Katharine of Aragon was in like case".[14] Chapuys reported that she "greatly rejoiced" at Katherine Howard's downfall and moved to Richmond Palace, one of her London estates, to be closer to the King.[15] Sceptical Chapuys thought that it was unlikely that Henry would take Anne back; after all, he had repudiated her on valid grounds, and rumours circulated that she was "fond of wine" and indulged "in other excesses".[16] Yet Anne and her adherents still hoped for reconciliation. Anne's brother, William of Cleves, sent his ambassador to the Archbishop of Canterbury to talk about Henry's possible re-marriage to Anne. The archbishop "cut him short, saying the matter was too important for him to discuss without command from the King", and fired off a letter to Henry.[17]

In early 1542, a book entitled *Remonstrance of Anne of Cleves* was published in France. It was a sensational work of someone who clearly wanted to see Anne reinstated to her former glory. Henry VIII was furious and ordered his ambassador in France to urge Francis I to suppress the book. When the ambassador broached the subject of this slanderous publication with the French King, Francis pretended he knew nothing of the book and thought that the Duke of Cleves, Anne's brother, probably had no idea about it either. At the same time, Francis revealed his true feelings about Henry's reconciliation with Anne: "The lady Anne is yet of age to bear children, and albeit the wind hath been contrary, it may fortune to turn."[18] But Henry never seriously contemplated taking Anne back, and, although he maintained that he would remain a widower after Katherine Howard's execution, soon another lady caught his eye.

NOTES

[1] *State Papers,* Volume 1, pp. 697-698.
[2] Ibid.
[3] Wymond Carew complained that his wages were lower than Jasper Horsey, Anne's steward. See more in S. B. Watkins, *Anne of Cleves*, p. 73.
[4] *Letters and Papers, Henry VIII,* Volume 16, n. 374, 421.
[5] Ibid., n. 1407.
[6] *Letters and Papers, Henry VIII,* Volume 16, n. 1410.
[7] Ibid., n. 1441.
[8] *State Papers,* Volume 1, p. 701.
[9] *Letters and Papers, Henry VIII,* Volume 16, n. 1414.
[10] Ibid., n. 1433.
[11] *State Papers,* Volume 1, p. 709.
[12] Agnes Strickland, *Lives of the Queens of England: From the Norman Conquest,* Volume 3, p. 83.
[13] TAVERNER, Richard (1505/6-75), of London, Norbiton, Surr. and Wood Eaton, Oxon. History of Parliament Online.
[14] *Letters and Papers, Henry VIII,* Volume 16, n. 1332.
[15] Ibid., n. 1359.
[16] *Calendar of State Papers, Spain,* Volume 6 Part 1, n. 209.
[17] *Letters and Papers, Henry VIII,* Volume 16, n. 1449.
[18] Ibid., Volume 17, n. 128.

CHAPTER 17: "VERY OLD AND GREY"

On 12 July 1543, Henry VIII married Katherine Parr, his sixth and final wife. After Katherine Howard's execution, it became treason to marry the King without confessing any past indiscretions beforehand. "There are few, if any, ladies at court nowadays likely to aspire to the honour of becoming one of the King's wives", wrote Chapuys with a hint of malicious glee.[1] At this point in his life, Henry was "already very stout and daily growing heavier, much resembling his maternal grandfather, King Edward, being about his age". He seemed "very old and grey" since he lost Katharine Howard to the executioner's axe.[2]

Anne of Cleves was shocked to learn that her former husband married a woman older and less attractive than her. Katherine Parr, who was in her early thirties, had no children from her two previous marriages, and Anne mused "that there is no hope of issue, seeing that she had none with her two former husbands".[3] Yet Katherine Parr was not barren, as she would have a child with her fourth husband. The problem was Henry. In April 1542, his physicians were heard saying that "they see that this King, whether he remarries or remains a widower, as he proposes, will not have other issue".[4]

In the 1544 Act of Succession, the possibility of Henry and Katherine having children was raised—these children would inherit the crown after Prince Edward, but it was standard practice in succession acts to include the offspring of the current marriage even if there was no hope of such offspring ever being born. The succession was fixed on Prince Edward and his future issue, and if he died without children, the crown was to pass to his half sisters, Mary and Elizabeth. Although the King referred to Katherine Parr as his "most dear and most entirely beloved wife" and appointed her as regent during his war campaign in France, from his point of view she was expendable.[5] It wasn't Katherine who appeared sitting next to Henry in the famous painting depicting *The Family of Henry VIII*, celebrating the 1544 Act of Succession.[6] It was Jane Seymour, mother of the King's only male heir, who was celebrated as the matriarch of the Tudor dynasty.

The lack of pregnancy in the new royal marriage provoked rumours that Henry VIII might take another wife. In February 1546, the imperial ambassador remarked that "there are rumours here of a new Queen, although I do not know why, or how true it may be. Some people attribute to it the sterility of the present Queen".[7] Charles Brandon's widow, Katherine, Dowager Duchess of Suffolk, was said to have been "in great favour", and the Queen appeared "somewhat annoyed at the rumours".[8] Yet rumours of a possible remarriage stemmed more from Henry's reputation of a much-married monarch than from his displeasure with Katherine's perceived barrenness. At this point in his life, Henry was likely impotent. Constant pain in his legs and open ulcers also made intimate relations awkward if not downright impossible.

Although it was treason to talk about Henry VIII's death, many privately commented upon the fact that he was "sickly and could not long endure".[9] "This King's life was really thought to be in danger, not from the fever but from the leg, which often troubles him because he is very stout and marvellously excessive in drinking and eating", wrote the French ambassador in 1541.[10] "He is not dead, but he will die one day suddenly", Baron Montague once boasted, adding, "His leg will kill him, and then we shall have jolly stirring".[11] He also said that "the King is full of flesh and unwieldy, and he cannot long continue with his sore leg".[12] Montague was executed for his remarks in 1539, condemned for his part in the Exeter Conspiracy.

"The King was much grown of his body, and he could not go up and down the stairs, but was let up and down by a device", Thomas Howard, Duke of Norfolk, confided to his mistress in the 1540s.[13] The mentioned "device" was a chair carried by the King's servants. An inventory of furniture in the Palace of Westminster in 1546 recorded "two chairs called trams for the King's Majesty to sit in, to be carried to and fro in his galleries and chambers".[14] In October 1546, imperial ambassador Van der Delft saw the King "passing in his chair".[15]

The most illustrative example of Henry VIII's expanding frame is offered by his armour. Maria Hayward, historian specialising in Tudor costume, traced the King's increasing girth by measuring the waistline of his armour at different periods in his life. In 1515, when he was twenty-four, Henry's waistline measured thirty-five and a half inches, while in 1539-40 it increased dramatically to fifty-two and a half inches.[16] It was said that Henry VIII was so corpulent that "three biggest men to be found could get inside his doublet".[17]

In addition to crippling obesity, the King also suffered from mood swings. "He will be out of his wit one day", Montague opined in the 1530s, referring to Henry's notorious propensity to outbursts of uncontrollable rage and capricious changes of his decisions.[18] The French ambassador de Marillac observed that “people worth credit say he is often of a different opinion in the morning than after dinner”.[19]

Katherine Parr, his last wife, was almost executed for heresy because she dared to talk about religion with the King. She felt comfortable enough to debate religion and the Bible with Henry, which means that the King didn’t show his displeasure outwardly. Once, when she left, he “expressed his displeasure” over Katherine’s propensity to lecture him to the conservative Bishop of Winchester, the Queen’s enemy.[20] Winchester grabbed the opportunity and accused the Queen of sympathising with the evangelical circle. Persuaded by Winchester’s tactics, Henry gave his permission for the bishop to investigate Katherine’s beliefs. At some point, the King confided in one of his physicians, either Thomas Wendy or George Owen, complaining that Katherine dared to lecture him and that her enemies demanded her head.

The Queen learned of the charges laid against her and staged a reconciliation with the King, visiting him in his bedchamber one evening when he entertained the gentlemen of his Privy Council. She did not want to instruct the King, as she was only a "silly, poor woman", but thought that small talk would help him to "pass over this painful time of your infirmity". The King accepted Katherine's submission and when Chancellor Thomas Wriothesley came the next day with the guards to arrest the Queen, Henry lashed out at him, calling him an "arrant knave, beast and fool".[21]

The King's fondness for his sixth wife led nineteenth-century historian Agnes Strickland to assume that this was because "Katherine was the most skilful and patient of nurses, and shrunk not from any office, however humble, whereby she could afford mitigation to the sufferings of her royal husband". Strickland went further, writing: "It is recorded of her, that she would remain for hours on her knees beside him, applying fomentations and other palliatives to his ulcerated leg, which he would not permit anyone to dress but her."[22] Yet this is clearly fiction.[23] There are no records of Katherine Parr playing the role of Henry VIII's nurse. The myth stems from the fact that Strickland assumed that Katherine "had already served an apprenticeship to the infirmities of sickness in her attendance on the deathbeds of her two previous husbands and had doubtless acquired the art of adapting herself to the humours of male invalids".[24] It was not a queen's duty to tend to her sick royal husband because he had an array of physicians and apothecaries who served him. Henry VIII had a tendency to isolate himself from his younger wives when he was sick and indisposed. Katherine wasn't with him when he died.

Henry VIII's final illness started in December 1546. The imperial ambassador Van der Delft reported that on 5 December 1546 the King pulled him aside and excused for a cancelled audience, confessing that "he had suffered from a sharp attack of fever, which had lasted in its burning stage for thirty hours, but that he was now quite restored". The perceptive ambassador was not fooled and recorded that Henry's "colour does not bear out the latter statement, and he looks to me greatly fallen away".[25] Around 10 December, the King cancelled his audience with the French ambassador, allegedly due to "such a cold that he could not speak", but the ambassador was sceptical since he saw the King hunting daily.[26] But it was not the hunting Henry was used to in his younger days, when his restless energy meant that he had to ride several horses during each escapade. Now, he was usually observing from a hilltop or hunting at Great Standing, a three-storey platform without walls used to either shoot at game or watch the bloody spectacle unfold.

Due to his deteriorating health, Henry VIII spent the Christmas season of 1546 alone in Whitehall Palace, propped against his embroidered cushions in a bed of estate. Queen Katherine Parr, together with her stepdaughters, Mary and Elizabeth, spent the festive season in Greenwich. The puzzled imperial ambassador noticed that Katherine had never before left the King on a solemn occasion like this. "I do not know what to think or suspect", he wrote to Charles V.[27]

The King was seen publicly for the last time on 17 January 1547, when he had two brief audiences with the French and Spanish ambassadors. His condition started to rapidly deteriorate, and ten days later he received Communion from one of his confessors. Although Henry's death was obviously imminent, his own physicians were afraid to tell him he was dying because they could be arrested for treason under the Treason Act by predicting the death of a King.

Sir Anthony Denny, one of Henry VIII's closest advisors and a personal friend, decided to tell his sovereign lord that he was on his deathbed and should prepare his soul to depart this world. He approached him and said that in "man's judgment you are not like to live", urging him to call for a confessor. The King believed that "the mercy of God is able to pardon me all my sins, yes, though they were greater than they be". Still, Henry was not in a hurry to call for a priest. Denny asked if the King would like to see "any learned man to confer withal and open his mind unto". Henry nodded and said, "If I had any, it should be Dr Cranmer, but I will first take a little sleep. And then, as I feel myself, I will advise you upon the matter". By the time Archbishop Thomas Cranmer was summoned, the King had lost the power of speech. Cranmer urged Henry to give him some sort of a sign that he put his trust in Christ's mercy; when the archbishop held the dying King's hand in his, the King suddenly "wring it as hard as he could". Cranmer and all those who encircled the King's bed took it as a sign that Henry VIII died in the faith of Christ.[28] The King expired on 28 January 1547 at about two o'clock in the morning and passed from history straight into legend. After thirty-eight years on the throne and six marriages, he had only one legitimate male heir, the nine-year-old Prince Edward, who succeeded his father as Edward VI.

What killed Henry VIII? Over the years, historians have proposed various diagnoses for the King's ailments. Syphilis, first suggested in the 1888 article by A.S. Currie, has been ruled out as Henry didn't display symptoms of this disease, wasn't treated with the customary mercury and his children didn't display symptoms of congenital syphilis.[29] However, a manuscript preserved in the British Library entitled *Dr Butts' Diary* shows that even if Henry VIII didn't suffer from syphilis, he was afflicted by some other disease of venereal origin or possibly suffered from a urinary tract infection. MS Sloane 1047 is a pharmacopoeia of plasters, lotions, waters, ointments, poultices and unguents compiled by royal physicians, with recipes devised by Henry VIII himself.[30] Among the remedies devised by Henry there are curious references to two medicines for the royal penis: "an ointment devised by the King's Majesty at Cawood, to dry excoriations and comfort the member, called the sweet ointment" and "the King's Grace's ointment made at St James to cool and dry, and comfort the member".[31] One of the King's physicians, Dr Walter Cromer, devised a plaster "to cease pain, and to delay heat, and to comfort the member." A plaster made by Doctors Chambers, Butts, Augustine and Cromer was to "resolve humours, and to cease pain, and to comfort the member".[32] The manuscript dates from the late 1530s, when the ulcers covering the King's legs began causing serious trouble, such as pain and gathering of the fluids. A reference to Anne of Cleves, for whom a plaster to "mollify, and resolve, comfort and cease pain of cold and windy causes" was devised, allows us to put forward the theory that it dates from 1539-40.[33] The many references to the King's painful ulcers further strengthen the notion that the manuscript entries started in the late 1530s.

It is also often overlooked that at least one of Henry's contemporaries believed he may have suffered from syphilis, and the King used medicine that was believed to be effective in curing this disease. George Constantine was an evangelical priest and former member of the household of Sir Henry Norris, who was executed alongside Anne Boleyn in 1536. In his 1539 written report of his conversation with Thomas Barlow, Dean of Westbury, Constantine wondered whether the King's "sore leg" could be treated with "guaiacum".[34] Guaiacum is known by many names, including lignum guaiacum, guaiac wood, guaiac resin, lignum vitae, and pockwood. In 1519, guaiacum wood was praised as a treatment of syphilis by German nobleman Ulrich von Hutten, who eventually died of the disease.[35] In fact, guaiacum was more popular than mercury as a cure for syphilis at the time, "becoming the remedy of physicians and their wealthy clients, while mercury remained the remedy of the poor".[36]

But to suggest that Henry VIII suffered from syphilis bordered on treason, and the dean with whom Constantine conferred about it replied: "But ye durst [dare] not." Constantine replied: "By God but I durst. What made it any matter for my life or twenty thousand such for the preservation of his life?" The dean suggested that Constantine should talk about it with the King's physician, Dr Butts, but Constantine said that "he forgot, and moreover, the physicians would not meddle with it, because none of the old authors wrote of it". Furthermore, it would have been advisable first to find "someone of the King's complexion that had a sore leg, and prove the effect on him".[37] Perhaps the King heard about Constantine's suggestion after all since he devised for himself a plaster "to heal ulcers without pain, made with pearl and the wood of ligni guaiaci [lignum vitae]."[38] In this case, the guaiacum was used for the King's ulcerated legs.

Medical historian Sir Arthur MacNalty proposed in 1952 that Henry suffered from osteomyelitis, a chronic septic infection of the thigh bone, likely caused by his 1536 jousting accident.[39] Scurvy, caused by a chronic lack of vitamin C in the King's diet, was suggested in 1989.[40] Cushing's syndrome, endocrine disease, was proposed by Robert Hutchinson, who pointed out that Henry displayed symptoms consistent with this disease, such as excessive obesity, depression, paranoia, fatigue, frequent headaches, impotence and slower healing of wounds.[41] In 2009, it was theorised that Henry "may have acquired venous hypertension as a result of deep vein thrombosis", caused by sport injuries or the tight garters he wore. Type II diabetes is also seen as likely diagnosis.[42] Varicose ulcer is often cited among Henry's ailments.[43]

It is unlikely that we will know what exact disease killed Henry VIII, but the wealth of primary source material reveals a plethora of health problems and the ways Henry tried to minimise his discomfort. The aforementioned *Dr Butts' Diary* opens a window into Henry VIII's bedchamber, giving us a rare glimpse into his medical issues. Thirty-two recipes are noted as being of "the King's Majesty's devise". The nature of the entries strongly suggests that Henry intended to use these recipes on himself. There is, for instance, a plaster that "resolves humours which there is swelling in the legs", and another one intended "to ease the pain and swelling about the ankles". Other remedies included: "a grain ointment devised by the King's highness to take away heat and indurations", "to heal ulcers without pain", "to cool inflammation" and "to resolve and ease pain".[44]

The most recent theory about the King's health posits that since many of the medicaments from this manuscript contained high dosages of lead in various forms, "absorbed lead from his medications might have been a major factor in King Henry's personality change".[45] The question that begs to be asked is this: Was there such a thing as Henry VIII's "personality change"? Recent medical theory proposes that Henry's symptoms of paranoia, mood swings and outbursts of anger may have been caused by McLeod syndrome that usually develops in individuals with a Kell-positive blood type. McLeod syndrome usually develops around the fortieth year and causes a variety of symptoms such as personality changes, depression and irrational behaviour.[46] Some historians believe that the 1536 accident at the tiltyard, when the fully armoured King was crushed beneath his horse and knocked unconscious, caused brain damage that ultimately led to dramatic personality change.[47] This theory hinges on two reports. On 12 February 1536, Rodolfo Pio da Carpi, Bishop of Faneza, who resided in France, wrote "that the King of England has had a fall from his horse, and was thought to be dead for two hours".[48] Dr Pedro Ortiz, Katharine of Aragon's former proctor in Rome, informed the emperor's wife: "The French King said that the King of England had fallen from his horse, and been for two hours without speaking."[49] Yet none of these men were eyewitnesses to the accident. Eustace Chapuys, imperial ambassador in England, wrote a detailed account of the accident but didn't mention that Henry was unconscious for two hours:

"On the eve of the Conversion of St Paul, the King being mounted on a great horse to run at the lists, both fell so heavily that everyone thought it a miracle he was not killed, but he sustained no injury."[50]

It is interesting to compare Henry VIII's jousting accident to two similar accidents suffered by his rival Francis I. In 1516, the French King had a fall from his horse that rendered him speechless for an hour. Seven years later he was thrown from his horse and knocked unconscious for two days. His life was in danger, and many believed that he would never recover, being paralysed on one side; "as touching his own person, either in wit or activity for the war, he is not like to do any great feat".[51] Contrary to such grim predictions, Francis recovered and suffered no greater physical consequences. There was also no personality change recorded.

One of Henry's biographers, J.J. Scarisbrick, rejected the idea that the King's brain was damaged in the 1536 jousting accident, arguing that "Henry was not notably more cruel afterwards than he had been before".[52] This is borne out by contemporary evidence. Henry ascended the throne on a wave of popular rejoicing and right in the beginning sent two of his father's unpopular advisers, Empson and Dudley, to the scaffold. In June 1535, the French King observed that Henry was "the hardest friend to bear in the world; at one time unstable, and at another time obstinate and proud, so that it was almost impossible to bear with him . . . in effect, he is the strangest man in the world".[53]

It's true that by the end of his reign Henry became tyrannical, unpredictable and was prone to mood swings, but these characteristics were already present in him when he was younger. Raised as a prince of royal blood, Henry was used to being served on bended knees and often, even as an adult, acted like a spoilt child. The simplest explanation of Henry's supposed personality change was the fact that by the 1540s he was already sick and corpulent, suffering terrible pain emanating from his ulcerated legs. He was a hulk of a man with two sick legs unable to support his obese body. Leafing through the manuscript with medicines devised by and for Henry, one cannot help but feel sorry for the man, reading recipes for medicaments to soothe the pain he was in.

NOTES

[1] *Calendar of State Papers, Spain,* Volume 6 Part 1, 1538-1542, n. 232.
[2] *Letters and Papers, Foreign and Domestic, Henry VIII,* Volume 17, n. 178.
[3] Ibid., Volume 18 Part, n. 954.
[4] Ibid., Volume 17, n. 248.
[5] Janel Mueller, *Katherine Parr: Complete Works and Correspondence,* pp. 52-53.
[6] https://www.rct.uk/collection/405796/the-family-of-henry-viii
[7] *Calendar of State Papers, Spain,* Volume 8, 1545-1546, n. 204
[8] Ibid.
[9] Edward Herbert, Baron Herbert of Cherbury, *The Life and Raigne of King Henry the Eighth*, p. 563.
[10] *Letters and Papers, Foreign and Domestic, Henry VIII,* Volume 16, n. 590.
[11] Ibid., Volume 13 Part 2, n. 979, 7.
[12] Ibid., n. 702, 2.
[13] Edward Herbert, Baron Herbert of Cherbury, *The Life and Raigne of King Henry the Eighth*, p. 563.
[14] Robert Hutchinson, *The Last Days of Henry VIII*, p. 122.
[15] *Letters and Papers, Foreign and Domestic, Henry VIII,* Volume 21 Part 2, n. 238.
[16] Maria Hayward, *Dress at the Court of Henry VIII*, p. 6.
[17] Ibid., p. 3.
[18] *Letters and Papers, Foreign and Domestic, Henry VIII,* Volume 13 Part 2, n. 979, 7.
[19] Ibid., Volume 16, n. 590.
[20] Janel Mueller, *Katherine Parr: Complete Works and Correspondence*, p. 23.
[21] John Foxe, *The Actes and Monuments of the Church*, pp. 615-618.
[22] Agnes Strickland, *Lives of the Queens of England: From the Norman Conquest,* Volumes 4-5, p. 49.
[23] David Starkey, *Six Wives: The Queen of Henry VIII*, p. 11.
[24] Agnes Strickland, op.cit.
[25] *Calendar of State Papers, Spain,* Volume 8, 1545-1546, n. 370.

[26] *Letters and Papers, Foreign and Domestic, Henry VIII,* Volume 21 Part 2, n. 517.

[27] *Calendar of State Papers, Spain,* Volume 8, 1545-1546, n. 370.

[28] J. J. Scarisbrick, *Henry VIII*, pp. 495-496.

[29] A. S. Currie, "Notes on the Obstetrical History of Catherine of Aragon and Anne Boleyn", *Edinburgh Medical Journal* 38 (1888), pp. 1-34.

[30] British Library, MS Sloane 1047.

[31] Ibid., f. 40r, ff. 42r-42v.

[32] Ibid., ff. 23r-24r.

[33] Ibid., f. 30v.

[34] *Letters and Papers, Henry VIII,* Volume 14 Part 2, n. 400.

[35] Jill Ann Grimes MD, Lori Apffel Smith MD, Kristyn Fagerberg MD, *Sexually Transmitted Disease*, p. 219.

[36] Lois N. Magner, *A History of Medicine*, p. 180.

[37] *Letters and Papers, Foreign and Domestic, Henry VIII,* Volume 14 Part 2, n. 400.

[38] British Library, MS Sloane 1047, ff. 5r-5v.

[39] Sir Arthur Salusbury MacNalty, *Henry VIII, a Difficult Patient,* p. 159.

[40] Susan Maclean Kybett, "Henry VIII - A Malnourished King?", *History Today 39* (September 1989), pp. 19-25.

[41] Robert Hutchinsonm, *The Last Days of Henry VIII*, p'. 205-2010.

[42] CR Chalmers and EJ Chaloner, "500 Years Later: Henry VIII, Leg Ulcers and the Course of History", *Journal of the Royal Society of Medicine*, 2009 Dec 1; 102(12): 514–517.

[43] J. J. Scarisbrick, *Henry VIII*, p. 485.

[44] British Library, MS Sloane 1047.

[45] A. Charlton, "A hypothesis: King Henry VIII's (1491–1547) Personality Change: A Case of Lead Poisoning?", *Journal of Medical Biography* 25(2), 72–80.

[46] Catrina Banks Whitley and Kyra Kramer, "A New Explanation For the Reproductive Woes and Midlife Decline of Henry VIII", *The Historical Journal*, Volume 53, No. 4 (December 2010), pp. 827-848.

[47] This theory is further discussed in Dr Suzannah Lipscomb's *1536: The Year that Changed Henry VIII*, pp. 23-26.

[48] *Letters and Papers, Foreign and Domestic, Henry VIII,* Volume 10, n. 294.

[49] Ibid., n. 427.

[50] Ibid., n. 200.

[51] *Letters and Papers, Foreign and Domestic, Henry VIII,* Volume 3, 1519-1523, n. 2833, 2846.

[52] J. J. Scarisbrick, *Henry VIII*, p. 485.

[53] *Letters and Papers, Foreign and Domestic, Henry VIII,* Volume 8, n. 837.

CHAPTER 18: "LIKE A CHILD OF HIS PUISSANCE"

Edward VI, Henry VIII's only legitimate son, had often been described as a sickly child. This assertion hinges partly on hindsight and partly on the French ambassador's reports. In October 1541, Charles de Marillac reported that he heard "the Prince was so fat and unhealthy as to be unlikely to live long".[1] When the ambassador saw the prince himself, however, he praised the boy as "handsome and well-nourished and wonderfully big for his age."[2] A portrait of Edward as a toddler, painted in 1538 by Hans Holbein, shows an adorable baby with reddish-blond hair, pouting lips and chubby cheeks, nothing out of the ordinary.

Prince Edward spent his early years mostly in the countryside, away from the pestilential London air. His royal household was established in March 1538, when Edward was five months old. Although he had a chamberlain, almoner and steward, among other male servants, his early upbringing was entrusted mostly to women. Apart from a wet nurse and four "rockers" who bounced his cradle to pacify him, Edward had a "lady mistress" who acted as a superintendent of his household. Lady Margaret Bryan served as lady mistress to all of Henry VIII's children and took affectionate, motherly care of them. In June 1538, she reported that Edward was "in good health and merry" and "hath four teeth, three full out and the fourth appearing".[3]

Influential members of Henry VIII's court and foreign ambassadors often applied for a licence to see the prince to show their allegiance to him and report about his health and appearance. In August 1538, the imperial ambassadors Chapuys and Mendoza described Edward as "the prettiest child we ever saw".[4] In September of that year, Sir Thomas Audley, Lord Chancellor, went to see Edward at Havering-atte-Bower and left an evocative pen-portrait of the King's son:

"I never saw so goodly a child of his age, so merry, so pleasant, so good, and loving countenance, and so earnest an yeah, as it were a sage judgment towards every person that repaired to His Grace; and, as it seemed to me, thanks be to our Lord, His Grace increased well in the air that he is in. And albeit a little His Grace's flesh decayed, yet he shoot out in length, and waxed firm and stiff, and can steadfastly stand, and would advance himself to move and go, if they would suffer him; but, as to me seemed, they do yet best, considering His Grace is yet tender, that he should not strain himself, as his own courage would serve him, till he comes above a year of age. I was right glad to understand there, that the King's Majesty will have His Grace removed from Havering, now against winter time; for surely it seemed to me that the house will be a cold house for winter; but, for summer, it is good, and a goodly air. I cannot comprehend nor describe the goodly, toward qualities, that is in my Lord Prince's Grace. He is sent of Almighty God for all our comforts. My daily and continual prayer is, and shall be, for his good and prosperous preservation, and to make His Grace an old Prince."[5]

Although his mother died two weeks after his birth, Edward was breastfed by a wet nurse and reportedly "sucketh like a child of his puissance".[6] In October 1538, he was weaned and a "dry nurse", Sybil Penn, was appointed to feed the prince and oversee lower servants in his household.[7] He was a happy and lively baby, as reported by people who interacted with him. When he was two years old, Lady Bryan wrote to Cromwell that the previous evening Edward was "marvellous pleasantly disposed" and "danced and played so wantonly that he could not stand still, and was as full of pretty toys as I ever saw child in my life".[8]

In October 1541, Edward "was sick of a quartan fever, an unusual malady for a child of three to four years, who is not of a melancholic complexion".[9] Henry VIII "summoned all the physicians of the country to advise" and they all agreed that high fever put the prince in grave danger. But Edward shook it off and survived. The incident reminded the King that his succession rested on the shoulders of a four-year-old boy. Indeed, in April 1542 the French ambassador reported that "doctors say that this young Prince of Wales is not of constitution to live long."[10]

When negotiating a possible French marriage for his elder daughter, Mary, in 1542, the King was reluctant to let her go because he feared that the French would rule through her and appropriate England if he and Edward died. He reminded the French ambassador that Mary had a kingdom to offer because "she had before her only the prince of Wales" who was "at such a young age that we can estimate him to be still only like a morning dew".[11]

By the time he married his sixth wife in 1543, Henry VIII was most likely impotent, and his physicians believed he wouldn't have more children. This is why the old King took such great care of his only son, making sure that the boy grew up in healthy surroundings. Members of Edward's household were strictly forbidden to visit London during periods when the plague was rife, and beggars (perceived as carriers of infectious diseases) seeking alms were ordered to keep away from the gates of the prince's palaces. Edward's rooms were to be spacious, bright and well-aired, and the prince himself was to exercise out in the fresh countryside air.

Edward was only nine years old when Henry VIII died, so he couldn't assume full power by himself. Edward Seymour, Duke of Somerset, the King's maternal uncle, assumed the role of Lord Protector and dominated the council and Edward's life for several years before his ultimate fall from grace and execution in 1552. Somerset was succeeded by John Dudley, Duke of Northumberland, who took on the role of Lord President of the Council. Although many perceived Edward as dominated by powerful men, the King's personality started to shine as he entered adolescence. "I carefully observed the King's face and manners", reported the watchful imperial ambassador Jehan Scheyfve in the aftermath of Somerset's execution in 1552, "and he seems to be a likely lad of quick, ready and well-developed mind; remarkably so for his age". He opined that the King "would become a very noteworthy prince".[12]

But it was not to be so, for Edward VI fell mortally ill in 1553. His illness started in January with a "tough strong straining cough".[13] In February, he was "attacked by a fever caused by a chill he had caught".[14] When Edward's elder half sister Mary visited him that month, Edward received her in the privacy of his bedchamber due to his illness. Edward's fever caused him difficulty in drawing breath, but this was said to have been because "his right shoulder is lower than his left and he suffers a good deal when the fever is upon him . . . due to the compression of the organs on the right side".[15] One month later, on 17 March, Edward was still sick:

"The King of England has never left his room since the beginning of the illness that came upon him not long ago. I have made inquiries whether his indisposition is likely to last long, and it appears that he is very weak and thin, besides which I learn from a good source that his doctors and physicians have charged the Council to watch him carefully and not move away from him, as they are of opinion that the slightest change might place his life in great danger."[16]

By 11 April, Edward had recovered enough to leave his chambers and "has gone out in his park at Westminster of late, but with the advice of his doctors and physicians, who assign him a definite hour, and still observe him strictly, especially his diet".[17] Later that month Edward moved to Greenwich Palace and walked in the gardens. Imperial ambassador Jehan Scheyfve, who took a keen interest in the King's health, wrote a series of detailed reports about what turned out to be Edward VI's final illness, lasting from April to July 1553.

On 28 April, Scheyfve observed that the fifteen-year-old King was "undoubtedly becoming weaker as time passes, and wasting away". "The matter he ejects from his mouth is sometimes coloured a greenish yellow and black, sometimes pink, like the colour of blood", he reported and added that the King's physicians were perplexed and did not know what to make of his symptoms.[18] As it dawned on him that he was dying, Edward VI drew up his "devise for the succession", a document that ultimately disinherited his half sisters, Mary and Elizabeth, and appointed his cousin Lady Jane Grey as his heiress. In the beginning of May 1553, several physicians met at Greenwich Palace to confer about the King's illness:

"Since my last letters of April 28th were written, the King's doctors and physicians conferred with his chief ministers over his illness. They requested very earnestly to be allowed to summon others of their art to consult with them and receive the assistance of their knowledge, as the King's life was in great danger. Six more were proposed, and three among them chosen, one of whom is the Duke of Northumberland's physician, another a certain professor of the University of Oxford, the third a Londoner. They have been strictly and expressly forbidden, under pain of death, to mention to anyone private details concerning the King's illness or condition. They took a solemn oath on it, in the presence of the following lords: the Duke of Northumberland, the Duke of Suffolk, the Marquis of Northampton, the Lord Treasurer and my Lord Chamberlain. I have certain information that the King is declining from day to day so rapidly that he cannot last long."[19]

Despite so many physicians attending him (or perhaps because of so many colliding opinions and treatments), Edward's health was rapidly deteriorating:

"The King is still indisposed, and it is held for certain that he cannot escape. The physicians are now all agreed that he is suffering from a suppurating tumour on the lung, or that at least his lung is attacked. He is beginning to break out in ulcers; he is vexed by a harsh, continuous cough, his body is dry and burning, his belly is swollen, he has a slow fever upon him that never leaves him."

Rumours swirled in London that Edward was dying, so his councillors started to spread reports of the King's recovery to appease the public. Three citizens who dared say that the King was dying or was already dead were apprehended and punished by having their ears clipped off.[20] On 20 May, Scheyfve reported a rumour that Edward "sinks very low from time to time", i.e. loses consciousness, "and his condition becomes desperate".[21] By 30 May 1553, the King's closest councillors accepted that there was no cure for Edward, and that he was on his deathbed:

"The King of England is wasting away daily, and there is no sign or likelihood of any improvement. Some are of opinion that he may last two months more, but he cannot possibly live beyond that time. He cannot rest except by means of medicines and external applications; and his body has begun to swell, especially his head and feet. His hair is to be shaved off and plasters are going to be put on his head."[22]

On 12 June, the imperial ambassador reported that Edward was attended by two physicians, "the other three, when they go to visit the King, examine his urine and excrements, but are not allowed to approach him".[23] It was widely believed that even the King's physicians were puzzled and visited him out of obligation, knowing that he was beyond saving. He continued on 15 June:

"The King is never quite free from fever, but on the 11th of this month he was attacked by a violent hot fever, which lasted over 24 hours, and left him weak and still feverish, though not as much so as at first. On the 14th, the fever returned more violent than before, and the doctors gave up the King and decided that he could not recover, but that about the 25th of this month, at the time of the full moon, he must decline to a point at which his life would be in the gravest danger, nay that he might die before that time, because he is at present without the strength necessary to rid him of certain humours which, when he does succeed in ejecting them, give forth a stench. Since the 11th, he has been unable to keep anything in his stomach, so he lives entirely on restoratives and obtains hardly any repose. His legs are swelling, and he has to lie flat on his back, whereas he was up a good deal of the time (i.e. before the violent attack of the 11th). They say it is hardly to be believed how much the King has changed since the 11th."[24]

By 19 June, Sheyfve had informed the emperor that Edward "has sunk so rapidly since my last letter of the 15th that the physicians no longer dare to answer for it that he will last one day more. His state is such that the King himself has given up hope, and says he feels so weak that he can resist no longer, and that he is done for".[25] On 24 June, Edward was so exhausted that his death was expected daily:

"I have this very instant been informed that the King of England's present condition is such that he cannot possibly live more than three days. It is firmly believed that he will die tomorrow, for he has not the strength to stir, and can hardly breathe. His body no longer performs its functions, his nails and hair are dropping off, and all his person is scabby."[26]

Edward's plans to cut Mary and Elizabeth out of the line of succession were now public, although they were still regarded as rumours. To quash reports of his death, the King showed himself in a window at Greenwich Palace, "where many saw him". He presented a sorry sight, "so thin and wasted that all men said he was doomed". Plans were made for Edward to show himself to the people again on Sunday, 2 July, "and a great crowd went to see [him], but they were told it should be done the following day". "A large gathering then assembled", but one of the gentlemen of the King's Bedchamber came and said that the air was "too chill" and the King wouldn't come. The imperial ambassador had no doubts that Edward's days were numbered:

"As far as I am able to ascertain, Sire, the King is very ill today [4 July] and cannot last long. He will die suddenly, and no one can foretell whether he will live an hour longer, notwithstanding his having been shown to the people, for that was done against the physicians' advice. It seems there is at present about the King a certain woman who professes to understand medicine, and is administering certain restoratives, though not independently of the physicians."[27]

The woman who visited Edward was probably a local healer. Edward's early biographer Sir John Hayward blamed her for the King's deterioration in health, writing that shortly after her visit "the King fell into desperate extremities, his vital parts were mortally stuffed [swollen], his legs swelled, his pulse failed, his skin changed colour and many other horrid symptoms appeared".[28]

When Edward VI—swollen, bald and covered in ulcerous bedsores—died on 6 July 1553, his death was initially kept secret from the public to allow a swift change of regime and the smooth passing of the crown to Lady Jane Grey. Lady Jane turned out to be an unpopular choice, and Edward VI's elder half sister, Lady Mary, made her own bid for the throne. Gathering an army to fight for her cause, she defeated Lady Jane's adherents without a single drop of blood being shed. She was proclaimed Queen on 19 July. Northumberland and his closest allies were immediately arrested for committing treason.

What killed Edward VI? In a letter to the English ambassadors abroad, the lords of the Privy Council wrote:

> "The disease whereof his Majesty died was the disease of the lungs, which had in them two great ulcers, and were putrefied, by means whereof he fell into a consumption, and so hath wasted, being utterly incurable."[29]

This statement was likely based on a postmortem examination of Edward's body. Writing in August 1554, the Venetian ambassador Giacomo Soranzo wrote that Edward "was seized with a malady, which the physicians soon knew to be consumption".[30] Another observer writing during

Elizabeth's reign said that "the physicians reported that he died of consumption; the same was affirmed by the grooms of his Privy Chamber, which did keep continual watch with the sick King".[31] It's thus reasonable to conclude that Edward's physicians ascribed the cause of his death to consumption, as tuberculosis was then known.

Details of Edward's symptoms started to leak out, and because most of these symptoms (swelling of the limbs, failing pulse, discoloration of the skin) weren't typical signs of tuberculosis, rumours spread that he was "gradually carried off by some slow poison administered long before [his death]".[32] Soon embellished reports started appearing; one of them claimed that Edward developed a "crazy cold" after drinking cold water from an infected cup following a tennis match.[33]Interestingly, over the course of Edward's illness it was said that the same disease had carried Henry FitzRoy to his early grave in 1536. FitzRoy, Edward's half brother, was said to have had "rapid consumption" in July 1536.[34] No other symptoms leaked, but after FitzRoy's death rumours spread that he had been poisoned by Anne Boleyn and her brother because "he pined inwardly in his body long before he died".[35] Henry VIII ordered FitzRoy's secret and subdued funeral, which strengthens the notion that he died of a quick and possibly infectious disease that disfigured his body. Edward's burial on 8 August 1553 was also not grand, with the imperial ambassadors attesting that they saw "the body of the late King carried to his grave with small ceremony".[36]

On 16 August 1553, John Burcher, a cloth merchant living in Strasbourg, wrote to Heinrich Bullinger of the curious rumour circulating in England:

"A writer worthy of credit informs me, that our excellent King has been most shamefully taken off by poison. His nails and hair fell off before his death, so that, handsome as he was, he entirely lost all his good looks. The perpetrators of the murder were ashamed of allowing the body of the deceased king to lie in state, and be seen by the public, as is usual: wherefore they buried him privately in a paddock adjoining the palace, and substituted in his place, to be seen by the people, a youth not very unlike him whom they had murdered. One of the sons of the duke of Northumberland acknowledged this fact."[37]

There's no evidence that Edward VI was buried in a paddock; he was buried at Westminster Abbey as befitted his rank and station.[38]

Today scholars give three possible causes of Edward VI's death: tuberculosis, suppurating pulmonary infection and bacterial pulmonary infection. In 2001, Doctors Grace Holmes, Frederick Holmes and Julia McMorrough suggested that Edward died of "rapidly progressive tuberculosis that developed after he had measles".[39] In April 1552, Edward contracted measles and then smallpox but "perfectly recovered" from both.[40] Although Edward recovered well, it's been suggested by medical experts that measles suppressed his immunity to tuberculosis. Modern research proves that symptoms such as failing pulse and swelling are indicative of tuberculous pericarditis, another possible cause of Edward's death.[41]

Edward VI's biographer Jennifer Loach suggested that the King contracted a suppurating pulmonary infection that ultimately led to renal failure.[42] In her biography of Mary Tudor, Dr Linda Porter proposed that the King contracted a bacterial pulmonary infection that weakened his organs and that this led to renal failure and septicaemia.[43] All historians are unanimous in the opinion that if he had lived in an era of antibiotics, Edward would have likely survived his final illness.[44]

NOTES

[1] *Letters and Papers, Henry VIII,* Volume 16, n. 1297.
[2] Ibid., n. 820.
[3] Ibid., Volume 13 Part 1, n. 1290.

[4] *Letters and Papers, Henry VIII,* Volume 13 Part 2, n. 232.
[5] *State Papers,* Volume 1, pp. 586-587.
[6] *Letters and Papers, Henry VIII,* Volume 12 Part 2, n. 1004.
[7] Ibid., Volume 13 Part 2, n. 524.
[8] M.A. Everett Wood, *Letters of Royal and Illustrious Ladies*, Volume 3, p. 112.
[9] *Letters and Papers, Henry VIII,* Volume 16, n. 1297.
[10] Ibid., Volume 17, n. 248.
[11] *Correspondance Politique de MM. De Castillon et de Marillac*, ed. M. Jean Kaulek, p. 406.
[12] *Calendar of State Papers, Spain,* Volume 10, 1550-1552, 14 January 1552.
[13] Sir John Hayward, *The Life and Raigne of King Edward the Sixth*, p. 177.
[14] *Calendar of State Papers, Spain,* Volume 11, 17 February 1553.
[15] Ibid.
[16] Ibid., 17 March 1553.
[17] Ibid., 10 April 1553.
[18] Ibid, 28 April 1553.
[19] Ibid., 5 May 1553.
[20] Ibid., 12 May 1553.
[21] Ibid., 20 May 1553.
[22] Ibid., 30 May 1553.
[23] Ibid., 12 June 1553.
[24] Ibid., 15 June 1553.
[25] Ibid, 19 June 1553.
[26] Ibid., 24 June 1553.
[27] Ibid., 4 July 1553.
[28] Sir John Hayward, *The Life and Raigne of King Edward the Sixth*, p. 177.
[29] Edmund Lodge, *Illustrations of British History*, Volume 1, p. 225.
[30] *Calendar of State Papers, Venice,* Volume 5, n. 934.
[31] Chris Skidmore, *Edward VI*, p. 351.
[32] Pietro Martire Vermigli, *Historical Narration of Certain Events*, p. 71.
[33] John Payne Collier, *Extracts*, p. 25.
[34] *Calendar of State Papers, Spain,* Volume 5 Part 2, n. 71.
[35] *Wriothesley's Chronicle*, Volume 1, pp. 53-4.
[36] *Calendar of State Papers, Spain*, Volume 11, 8 August 1553.
[37] *The Parker Society for the Publication of the Works of the Fathers and Early Writers of the Reformed English Church,* Volume 53, p. 684.
[38] *Calendar of State Papers, Spain,* Volume 11, 8 August 1553.

[39] Grace Holmes, Frederick Holmes, and Julia McMorrough, "The Death of Young King Edward VI", *New England Journal of Medicine*, 345: 1 (2001): 60-62.

[40] Sir John Hayward, *The Life and Raigne of King Edward the Sixth,* p. 168.

[41] Grace Holmes, Frederick Holmes, and Julia McMorrough, op.cit.

[42] Jennifer Loach, *Edward VI*, p. 162.

[43] Linda Porter, *Mary Tudor: The First Queen*, p. 184-186.

[44] Ibid.

CHAPTER 19: "IN MEAN STATE OF HEALTH"

Mary Tudor, born on 18 February 1516, was the only child of Henry VIII's marriage to Katharine of Aragon who survived the perils of childhood and lived to adulthood. Yet although she was born into wealth and privilege, Mary's world was turned upside down when Henry VIII decided to divorce her mother. Her parents' divorce shattered Mary's world. She was only eleven in 1527, when Henry VIII revealed his plans to abandon Katharine of Aragon and marry Anne Boleyn. The years between the beginning of Henry VIII's quest for divorce in 1527 and her mother's death in 1536 were Mary's formative years. As a result of the stress she went through as a girl on the verge of puberty, Mary started suffering from irregular and painful menstruations, insomnia, migraines and depression.

Mary's illnesses during the period between 1527 and 1536 were largely psychosomatic. In April 1531, the Venetian ambassador reported that she was "very ill from what the physicians call hysteria".[1] The word "hysteria" was not actually used in the original Italian report as the term was coined much later in the nineteenth century. The original sixteenth-century text said that Mary suffered from "what the physicians call 'the mother'".[2] "The mother" was a reference to a female illness connected to irregular or suppressed menstruations, causing the womb to suffocate or choke. "The mother" was considered a disease of the womb, called *hystera* in Greek. Imperial ambassador Chapuys wrote on 29 April 1531 that she was recovering "from her stomach attack" but in June Mary was ill again.[3] The Milanese ambassador wrote: "She has been very ill these last days, so that they had to let blood; the trouble being with her womb."[4]

Mary's problems coincided with her mother's banishment from court. Still, despite her health problems, Mary was in her prime. Italian visitor Mario Savorgnano described her thus:

"This Princess is not very tall, has a pretty face, and is well proportioned with a very beautiful complexion, and is fifteen years old. She speaks Spanish, French, and Latin, besides her own mother-English tongue, is well grounded in Greek, and understands Italian, but does not venture to speak it. She sings excellently, and plays on several instruments, so that she combines every accomplishment."[5]

In January 1533, Henry VIII married the already pregnant Anne Boleyn and had his marriage to Katharine of Aragon annulled four months later. Katharine was demoted from Queen to Dowager Princess of Wales, a title that she never accepted. Anne was crowned in June 1533, and in September of that year she gave birth to her daughter, Elizabeth. Shortly after Elizabeth's birth, Mary was informed that she was no longer princess and had no right to the throne. Declared illegitimate and unfit to succeed her father, Mary was further humiliated by having her royal household reduced and incorporated into Elizabeth's. In December 1533, when Mary arrived to Elizabeth's household, she was asked to pay respects to her half sister, but she replied that "she knew no other Princess in England except herself, and that the daughter of Madame Pembroke [Anne Boleyn] had no such title". Yet despite this outward bravado, Mary "retired to weep in her chamber, as she does continually".[6]

During her spectacular rise to power Anne Boleyn made no effort to befriend Mary, and if the imperial ambassador Chapuys was truthful, Anne was bitterly jealous of the King's feelings towards his daughter and made it clear that she didn't want Henry and Mary to keep close contact.

Two lady mistresses served in the joint household of Mary and Elizabeth. Mary's lady governess was Anne Shelton, Anne Boleyn's aunt, who was instructed to slap Mary across her face and box her ears if she insisted to be called princess. Following Elizabeth's birth, the King kept Mary at a physical and emotional distance, depriving her not only of her titles but also of her favourite servants, including Margaret Pole, Countess of Salisbury, former superintendent of Mary's household.

The new Act of Succession in 1534 proclaimed issue between Henry VIII and Anne Boleyn as fit to inherit the throne, and Mary was effectively disinherited. Although the act was enforced by an oath of allegiance promulgated by Parliament in the same year, neither Katharine nor Mary yielded. Refusal was equivalent to treason; the most famous victims of the act were Bishop John Fisher and Sir Thomas More, who refused to accept Henry VIII as head of the Anglican Church and swear an oath to uphold the Act of Succession passed in March. They refused to take the oath because it included the abjuration of the pope's authority. Fisher and More were executed on 22 June and 6 July 1535 respectively.

All of these events took their toll on Mary Tudor's mental and physical health. In September 1534, Mary's health deteriorated to the point that Henry VIII sent her his own physician, Dr William Butts, and allowed Katharine of Aragon to visit, although he had previously banned any contact between mother and daughter.[7] Dr Butts found Mary "in mean state of health, but at the beginning of her old disease".[8] In February 1535, Mary fell "dangerously ill", so much so that her life was at risk. Mary's sickness was caused by the looming threat of death or imprisonment if she wouldn't accept her mother's demoted title and her father as the head of the Anglican Church. Imperial ambassador Chapuys wrote that the King "desired I would choose one or two physicians to go to her along with his own" to avoid suspicions of ill treatment that Chapuys could report to Charles V. He further explained:

"For the same reason he would not allow his physicians to meddle with the case without the assistance of others—indeed, his physicians refused altogether to do so—and that sometime since they had written to the Queen's physician, who always excused himself, to wash his hands of it, and that the King was as much grieved at her sickness as any father could be for his daughter."[9]

In March 1535, Thomas Cromwell described Mary as "sickly and mortal".[10] The following month Katharine of

Aragon complained to Charles V: "My daughter has been ill, and has not yet recovered. Her treatment would suffice to make a healthy person ill." She wanted to take care of Mary herself, hoping this would restore Mary's health.[11]

After More's and Fisher's executions in the summer of 1535, Mary fell ill again. Imperial ambassador Eustace Chapuys implored the King to send his physician to Mary "both on account of a certain rheum, and to provide against a return of her ordinary complaint, which she dreads, in the coming winter".[12] It was widely believed that the King would send both Mary and her mother to their deaths. While Katharine embraced the idea of martyrdom, Mary's health deteriorated further. She was told that Anne Boleyn blamed her for the pending war with Charles V and said: "She is my death and I am hers; so I will take care that she shall not laugh at me after my death."[13]

On 7 January 1536, Katharine of Aragon died at Kimbolton Castle. Although she begged the King to let her see Mary on her deathbed, Henry denied her. Katharine's death plunged Mary into depression, and she was said to have been "mortally ill".[14] Again, this was a psychosomatic illness, and on 15 January Chapuys wrote that although Mary "recovered in body . . . her mind is afflicted by her mother's death".[15]

In May 1536, another shocking event took place at court: Anne Boleyn was executed for adultery, incest and treason. Like Mary, Elizabeth was declared illegitimate. Mary hoped that Anne's death would pave the way towards reconciliation with her father, but she was shocked when she learned that this was not to be. The King demanded of Mary to accept him as the head of the Church of England; this would require Mary to renounce the pope's authority and accept that her parents' marriage was illegal. Over the course of the negotiations of her submission to the King, she wrote to Cromwell a number of letters, informing him in one of them that "the rheum in my head will suffer me to write no more at this time".[16] In July 1536, Mary was finally reconciled with Henry VIII, but on her father's terms: she accepted, at least outwardly, that she was illegitimate. Deep down in her heart, Mary resented her father for the years of mistreatment, and depression was still gnawing at her.

Although Henry VIII kept marriage negotiations for Mary open until the end of his reign, she knew he did so only to maintain the old alliances or build new ones. The King's greatest fear was that if he or his heir died before Mary, any man she married would rule as de facto King of England. She once said "that it was folly to think that they would marry her out of England, or even in England, as long as her father lived . . . for she would be, while her father lived, only lady Mary, the most unhappy lady in Christendom".[17]

In 1541, when Mary was in her mid-twenties, her hand in marriage was offered to Francis I's son, Charles of Valois, Duke of Orléans. The French King wanted to know everything about Mary's appearance, health and education, instructing his ambassador Charles de Marillac to:

"[S]ee lady Mary and consider her stature and beauty and other things by which it may be judged whether she is [one] to bear children; also discreetly inquire, of her physicians if possible, if this melancholy which she has so long worn has not brought on some malady which might prevent her having issue, as is said."[18]

"She is of middle stature, and is in face like her father, especially about the mouth, but has a voice more manlike, for a woman, than he has for a man", de Marillac observed. Mary's rough, manly voice was remarked upon by more than one contemporary; it may be indicative of Mary's hormonal imbalance. "With a fresh complexion she looks not past eighteen or twenty although she is twenty-four", he enthused, adding that her "beauty is mediocre, and it may be said that she is one of the beauties of this Court". He further added about Mary's constitution and habits:

"She is active, and apparently not delicate, loving morning exercise and walking often two or three miles. She speaks and writes French well. Saw letters of hers in French, written to the Emperor's ambassador in the time of her 'ennuy.' She understands Latin and enjoys books of 'lettres humaines', which were her solace in sleepless nights at the time she was molested. She delights in music and plays the spinet singularly. In conversation, together with sweetness and benignity, she is prudent and reserved."

De Marillac secretly interviewed "a woman who has served in her chamber from her infancy, and is married to a Frenchman who is familiar with all the French ambassadors". She told de Marillac that "when her mother was first repudiated" in 1531, Mary "was sick with 'ennuy' but, on being visited and comforted by the King, soon recovered and has had no such illness since".[19] This "ennuy" was most likely depression, as it was allegedly alleviated by the King's comforting presence. Although Mary's chamber woman claimed that Mary didn't suffer from this illness anymore, other accounts tell a different story. Mary's health continued to deteriorate over the course of Henry VIII's reign.

In mid-April 1542, Chapuys wrote that she "suffers still from palpitation of the heart".[20] Later that month she fell sick again. De Marillac informed Francis I that "Madame Marie is dangerously ill of a strange fever since Easter, and takes such weakness at times that she remains as though dead".[21] This illness may have been infectious as several court members fell ill as well, including Anne of Cleves, who had tertian fever, Prince Edward and the Duke of Norfolk. In May, de Marillac reported that Mary "is much better, and, the doctors say, out of danger."[22] In 1543, Mary had "colic", and in 1544 she informed her friend Anne, Countess of Hertford, "I have been nothing well as yet these holidays; wherefore I pray you hold me excused that I write not this to you with my hand".[23] She paid her apothecaries for various medicines they made to alleviate her symptoms.

In October 1552, Mary received a letter from her half sister, Elizabeth. Addressing her as "my well-beloved sister Mary", Elizabeth expressed sadness at the state of her half sister's fragile health: "As to hear of your sickness is unpleasant to me, so it is nothing fearful, for that I understand it is your old guest that is wont oft to visit you, whose coming, though it be oft, yet it is never welcome."

Elizabeth was referring to Mary's recurrent affliction that always occurred "at the fall of the leaf".[24] This phrase suggests that this recurrent illness happened during autumn. Judith M. Richards suggested that this was a "seasonal allergic reaction", but the letter written by Mary herself in November 1550 shows this is not the case.[25] In the letter addressed to an unknown recipient, Mary gave her own account of this mysterious illness, denying any suggestions that it was caused by "soil" or "air":

"My Lord, I most heartily thank you for your gentle and kind letters. And where it should seem to you and others, my friends, that the soil and air of this house [Beaulieau] might be occasion of my sickness, for the recovery whereof you think good that I should remove from the same; my Lord, the truth is, that neither the house nor air is herein to be suspected but the time of the year being the fall of the leaf, at which time I have seldom escaped the same disease these many years; and the rather to prove the air not to be evil, I have not at the present (thanks be to God!) any of my household sick."[26]

Remembering that Mary suffered from "melancholy" since she was a teenager, this "old guest" occurring "at the fall of the leaf" appears to have been depression.

Depression has a tendency to develop in the autumn; it is then known as Seasonal Affective Disorder (SAD). Today it is recognised as part of a major depressive disorder.[27] As we have seen earlier in this chapter, in 1534 and 1535 two independent sources mentioned Mary's "old disease" and "a return of her ordinary complaint, which she dreads, in the coming winter". Both were likely referring to the fact that Mary exhibited stronger than usual symptoms of depression during the bleak winter months.[28]

That Mary's disease was psychological in nature is further attested by the report of Edward VI's councillors, who went to Mary in 1551 to admonish her for hearing Catholic Mass in her household. Religion was something that Mary felt strongly about and she refused to give up her Catholic faith. They reported that Mary's "colour often altered, and she seemed "passioned and unquiet", so they "forbore to trouble her further, fearing that the troubling her might bring on an attack of her old disease".[29]

Was Mary's depression a result of her upbringing, or did she have a genetic propensity for mental instability? Mental illness ran in both her paternal and maternal lineages. Catherine of Valois, Mary's great-great-grandmother who married Owen Tudor, the founding father of the Tudor dynasty, was born into a family with a history of mental illness. Catherine's father, the French King Charles VI, experienced hallucinations, delusions and at one point believed he was made of glass, forbidding anyone to come near him for fear he would shatter into pieces. He also believed that he was bewitched, as mental illness was not understood then as it is now. During his psychotic episodes, Charles refused to bathe, change clothes or sleep properly, and he also ran from his servants to the point of collapse. The exact nature of his illness remains unknown, with scholars point either to schizophrenia or a chronic manic-depressive illness.[30]

Charles's mother, Joanna of Bourbon, suffered a severe mental collapse after she gave birth to her seventh child, although her mental condition may have been triggered by childbirth, plunging her into postpartum depression or psychosis. Contemporaries recorded only that she "lost her good sense and her good memory" but recovered within months; her condition must have been serious since her husband, Charles V, went on a pilgrimage and offered many prayers for her recovery.[31]

Catherine of Valois's son, Henry VI of England, inherited his French grandfather's illness. In 1453, when he was thirty-two, Henry suffered a complete mental breakdown that left him unresponsive for a year and a half. An eyewitness recorded that "he completely lost his wits and memory for a time, and nearly all his body was so uncoordinated and out of control that he could neither walk, nor hold his head upright, nor easily move from where he sat".[32] Royal physicians applied potions, waters, laxatives, head-purges, gargles, bloodletting and incisions, among others, to rouse the King from his stupor. Nothing helped, but on Christmas Day 1454 Henry VI recovered, having no recollection of the past eighteen months. In October 1455, rumours circulated in England that Henry VI had relapsed into his illness. The nature of his affliction is a mystery, with schizophrenia proposed as one of the likeliest explanations. Henry VI never experienced as severe a form of mental instability as the one that plagued his grandfather, leading his recent biographer to wonder whether he "was suffering from a particularly severe episode of depression".[33]

Mary Tudor's maternal aunt, Joanna of Castile ("Joanna the Mad") was mentally unstable throughout her entire life, although she experienced periods of lucidity. The exact nature of Joanna's illness is unknown; in the past, historians suggested schizophrenia, severe depression or even dementia.[34] One contemporary, Peter Martyr, said that

Joanna was "lost in love for her spouse", giving rise to a theory that she wasn't mentally unstable but passionately in love with and thus pathologically jealous of her husband, Philip the Fair.[35] Isabella of Castile often worried about her daughter's mental health and once ordered Philip to "curb her and to restrain her from doing the things that her passion can lead her to do, and to keep her from doing anything that will bring danger or dishonour to her person".[36] Joanna was separated from her husband in 1504 and lost her appetite, hardly ever slept and experienced a psychotic episode that worried observers.

Then, as now, people wondered about Joanna's mental state but couldn't reach definitive conclusions. She certainly inherited a genetic propensity towards fragile mental health because her maternal grandmother was mentally unstable. Additionally, the many pregnancies Joanna went through during her marriage heightened her tendency towards anxiety as evidenced by her husband's comment that "when pregnant she sometimes becomes annoyed without cause".[37] One of Ferdinand of Aragon's envoys described Joanna as "an intelligent woman, of great spirit and very proud" with "a melancholy and haughty nature". He also observed that she was "jealous of her husband".[38]

With so many examples of mental instability in Mary Tudor's family tree, it's not surprising that she too succumbed to depression. Perhaps if her formative years hadn't been marred by insecurity, fear for her life and brutal emotional treatment by her father, she would have had less chance to experience mental breakdown.

NOTES

[1] *Calendar of State Papers, Venice,* Volume 6, 1555-1558, n. 884.
[2] Ibid. See also Judith M. Richard's "Reassessing Mary Tudor: Some Concluding Points" in *Mary Tudor: Old and New Perspectives*, p. 213.
[3] *Letters and Papers, Foreign and Domestic, Henry VIII,* Volume 5, n. 216.
[4] *Calendar of State Papers and Manuscripts in the Archives and Collections of Milan 1385-1618*, n. 865.
[5] *Calendar of State Papers Relating To English Affairs in the Archives of Venice,* Volume 4, n. 682.
[6] *Letters and Papers, Foreign and Domestic, Henry VIII,* Volume 6, n. 1558.
[7] *Letters and Papers, Henry VIII,* Volume 7, n. 1193.
[8] Ibid., n. 1129.
[9] Ibid., Volume 8, n. 189.
[10] Ibid., n. 355.
[11] Ibid., n. 514.
[12] Ibid., Volume 9, n. 287.
[13] Ibid., n. 873.
[14] Ibid., Volume 10, n. 133.
[15] Ibid., n. 106.
[16] Jean Mary Stone, *The History of Mary I*, p. 40.
[17] *Letters and Papers, Foreign and Domestic, Henry VIII*, Volume 17, n. 371.
[18] Ibid., Volume 16, n. 1186.
[19] Ibid., n. 1253.
[20] Ibid., Volume 17, n. 251.
[21] Ibid., n. 261.
[22] Ibid., n. 290.
[23] Ibid., Volume 18, n. 156 and Volume 19, n. 620.

[24] *Elizabeth I: Collected Works,* ed. Leah S. Marcus, Janel Mueller, Mary Beth Rose, pp. 37-8.

[25] Judith M. Richards, "Reassessing Mary Tudor: Some Concluding Points" in *Mary Tudor: Old and New Perspectives*, p. 213.

[26] Patrick Fraser Tytler, *England Under the Reigns of Edward VI and Mary I*, Volume 1, pp. 346-347.

[27] *Elizabeth I: Collected Works,* ed. Leah S. Marcus, Janel Mueller, Mary Beth Rose, pp. 37-8.

[28] For more about SAD, see Halszka Oginska, Katarzyna Oginska-Bruchal, "Chronotype and Personality Factors of Predisposition to Seasonal Affective Disorder", *Chronobiology International*, 31 (4): 523–31.

[29] Agnes Strickland, *Lives of the Queens of England, from the Norman Conquest (1868)*, Volume 2, p. 546.

[30] Rachel C. Gibbons, *The Active Queenship of Isabeau of Bavaria, 1392-1417*, p. 33.

[31] Basil Fulford Lowther Clarke, *Mental Disorder in Earlier Britain: Exploratory Studies*, p. 188.

[32] *Wethamsted's Register,* as cited in K. Dockray (ed.), A Source Book, p. 6.

[33] Lauren Johnson, *Shadow King: The Life and Death of Henry VI*, p. 234.

[34] Gillian B. Fleming, *Juana I: Legitimacy and Conflict in Sixteenth Century Castile*, pp. 6-7.

[35] Pedro Martir, *Epistolario: Estudio y Traduccion*, Volume 9, p. 222.

[36] Nancy Rubin, *Isabella of Castile: The First Renaissance Queen*, p. 405.

[37] Aram, p. 336.

[38] Gillian B. Fleming, *Juana I: Legitimacy and Conflict in Sixteenth Century Castile*, p. 84.

CHAPTER 20: "THINKING MYSELF TO BE WITH CHILD"

Mary ascended the throne on a wave of popular rejoicings in July 1553. She quickly made it clear that although she was sickly and old by the standards of her era, she wanted to marry and produce heirs to the throne. Her choice of a husband met with strong opposition from her council as well as the populace. In early 1554, Mary faced one of the biggest threats to her reign, Wyatt's Rebellion, but quashed it successfully. In July 1554, she married her kinsman, Philip of Spain, son of Emperor Charles V.

Mary's bridegroom, Philip of Spain, was born on 21 May 1527 to Charles V, Holy Roman Emperor, and Isabella of Portugal. Before he married Isabella, Charles himself had been briefly engaged to Mary, his first cousin, when she was a child. A miniature of Mary as princess showing her with a brooch with the inscription "The Emperor" pinned on her bodice still survives.[1] The Anglo-Imperial alliance of the 1520s didn't last long, but Mary remembered Charles V, whom she had met in 1522 during his visit to England, and revered him as a father figure later in her life. Philip, eleven years younger than Mary, had been married before. His first wife, Maria Manuela of Portugal, died after giving birth to their only son, Don Carlos, in 1545.

Mary instantly fell in love with Philip. His portraits show a good-looking young man of athletic build, with a luscious beard and sensual full lips. An enthusiastic eyewitness described Philip's appearance in glowing terms:

"Of visage he is well favoured, with a broad forehead and grey eyes, straight-nosed and of manly countenance. From the forehead to the point of his chin his face groweth small; his pace is princely, and gait so straight and upright as he loseth no inch of height; with a yellow head and a yellow beard . . . He is so well proportioned of body, arm and leg, and every other limb to the same, as nature cannot work a more perfect pattern."[2]

Mary was ten years Philip's senior but looked much older than her thirty-eight years merited. One anonymous member of Philip's entourage criticised Mary's appearance, saying that she was "not at all beautiful: small, and rather flabby than fat, she is of white complexion and fair, and has no eyebrows".[3] Venetian ambassador Giacomo Soranzo, writing at the same time, was kinder when he reported:

"She is of low stature, with a red and white complexion, and very thin; her eyes are white and large, and her hair reddish; her face is round, with a nose rather low and wide and were not her age on the decline she might be called handsome rather than the contrary. She is not of a strong constitution, and of late she suffers from headache and serious affection of the heart, so that she is often obliged to take medicine, and also to be blooded. She is of very spare diet, and never eats until 1 or 2 p.m., although she rises at daybreak, when, after saying her prayers and hearing mass in private, she transacts business incessantly, until after midnight, when she retires to rest . . ."[4]

The most detailed description of Mary comes from Giovanni Michieli, Venetian ambassador, who described her appearance and mental health:

"She is of low rather than of middling stature, but, although short, she has no personal defect in her limbs, nor is any part of her body deformed. She is of spare and delicate frame, quite unlike her father, who was tall and stout; nor does she resemble her mother, who, if not tall, was nevertheless bulky.

"Her face is well formed, as shown by her features and lineaments, and as seen by her portraits. When younger she was considered, not merely tolerably handsome, but of beauty exceeding mediocrity. At present, with the exception of some wrinkles, caused more by anxieties than by age, which make her appear some years older, her aspect, for the rest, is very grave.

"Her eyes are so piercing that they inspire, not only respect, but fear, in those on whom she fixes them, although she is very short-sighted, being unable to read or do anything else unless she has her sight quite close to what she wishes to peruse or to see distinctly. Her voice is rough and loud, almost like a man's, so that when she speaks she is always heard a long way off.

"In short, she is a seemly woman, and never to be loathed for ugliness, even at her present age, without considering her degree of queen. But whatever may be the amount deducted from her physical endowments, as much more may with truth, and without flattery, be added to those of her mind, as, besides the facility and quickness of her understanding, which comprehends whatever is intelligible to others, even to those who are not of her own sex (a marvellous gift for a woman), she is skilled in five languages, not merely understanding, but speaking four of them fluently, viz., English, Latin, French, Spanish, and

Italian, in which last, however, she does not venture to converse, although it is well known to her; but the replies she gives in Latin, and her very intelligent remarks made in that tongue surprise everybody. Besides woman's work, such as embroidery of every sort with the needle, she also practises music, playing especially on the clavichord and on the lute so excellently that, when intent on it (though now she plays rarely), she surprised the best performers, both by the rapidity of her hand and by her style of playing. Such are her virtues and external accomplishments."

As to Mary's mental health, Michieli observed that "with the exception of certain trifles, in which, to say the truth, she is like other women, being sudden and passionate, and close and miserly, rather more so than would become a bountiful and generous queen, she in other respects has no notable imperfections". Michieli also noted that Mary's "thoughts and passions, both public and private . . . often subject her to a very deep melancholy, much greater than that to which she is constitutionally liable, from menstruous retention and suffocation of the matrix to which for many years she has been often subject, so that the remedy of tears and weeping, to which from childhood she has been accustomed, and still often used by her, is not sufficient; she requires to be blooded either from the foot or elsewhere, which keeps her always pale and emaciated".[5]

Mary's bridegroom, Philip, confided to one of his Spanish servants that Mary was "no good from the point of view of fleshly sensuality". He found her plain and unattractive. One of the members of Philip's entourage, Ruy Gómez de Silva, empathised with his royal master when he wrote that "it would take God himself to drink this cup", referring to the sexual relations of the couple, adding that "the best one can say is that the King realises fully that the marriage was made for no fleshly consideration, but in order to cure the disorders of this country and to preserve the Low Countries". Still, Philip did his best to assure Mary that his feelings for her were genuine. "He treats the Queen very kindly", wrote one Spaniard, admiring the fact that Philip did his best to pass over the fact that Mary was not beautiful at all. "He makes her so happy", he continued, "that the other day when they were alone she almost talked love-talk to him, and he replied in the same vein".[6]

In the autumn of 1554, Mary was said to have been pregnant. On 20 December, the elated Queen wrote to her father-in-law, Charles V, that she felt the baby's movements:

"As for that which I carry in my belly, I declare it to be alive, and with great humility thank God for His great goodness shown to me, praying Him so to guide the fruit of my womb that it may contribute to His glory and honour, and give happiness to the King, my Lord and your son, to your Majesty, who were my second father in the lifetime of my own father, and are therefore doubly my father, and lastly that it may prove a blessing to this realm."[7]

Mary "took to her chamber" in anticipation of the birth of her heir on 20 April 1555. Imperial ambassador Simon Renard wrote to Charles V:

"The Queen has withdrawn, and no one enters her apartments except the women who serve her and who have the same duties as the court officials. This is an ancient custom in England whenever a princess is about to be confined: to remain in retirement forty days before and forty days after. However, it is believed that she will be delivered before the ninth day of next month. She would have liked to go to Windsor, but as that place is far from London, it was thought preferable that she should stay at Hampton Court. Troops will be at hand in case they are needed."[8]

The Queen was expected to give birth by 9 May 1555, but the date came and went, and no baby was born. Physicians were summoned to confer with the Queen, and they reached the verdict that she had miscalculated her due date, and the child was now expected to be born before 6 June 1555. "Everything in this kingdom depends on the Queen's safe deliverance", Renard mused in a letter to Charles V. Yet still no baby was born by 6 June. "The Queen's delivery keeps us all greatly exercised in our minds", wrote Ruy Gómez de Silva in early June 1555.[9]

In the first weeks of June, the clergy began to lead daily processions for the Queen's safe delivery. Mary observed these processions from the small window of her bedchamber each day, "most courteously bowing her head in acknowledgment to all the personages". The Venetian ambassador Michieli saw Mary and wrote that she was "looking very well", but others were not so sure.[10]

Antoine de Noailles, the French ambassador, learned from the Queen's midwife and one of her chief ladies that Mary was not pregnant because she had often sat on the floor of her chamber with knees drawn up to her chin, a position no pregnant woman could endure without considerable pain. Midwives and physicians were fearful to tell Mary the truth, and so she continued in her false hope. Simon Renard could not believe it, and on 24 June informed the emperor that Mary's "doctors and ladies have proved to be out in their calculations by about two months, and it now appears that she will not be delivered before eight or ten days from now".[11]

By now, the Queen was under pressure to deliver her child as soon as possible. Mary's delivery was "most earnestly desired by everybody, and principally by the King, who awaits nothing but this result in order to cross the Channel instantly, for, from what I hear, one single hour's delay in this delivery seems to him a thousand years".[12] Philip was expected at Flanders in August, and he could not bear to remain in England any longer. He started dissolving his Spanish household and sending his servants abroad, to Mary's utter disappointment.

In the privacy of her chambers, Mary prayed fervently for a favourable outcome of her pregnancy. Her prayer book, where the page devoted to intercessions for women with child is said to be stained with tears, survives at the British Library, a testament to Mary's faith and a sad reminder of her unfulfilled hope of becoming a mother. At the end of June 1555, even Mary's friend Cardinal Pole laughingly informed the Venetian ambassador that "I know not whether she be or be not pregnant".[13] "If God is pleased to grant her a child, things will take a turn for the better", Renard wrote to Charles V. "If not, I foresee trouble on so great a scale that the pen can hardly set it down".[14]

In July, Mary still asserted she was pregnant, although it had been three months since she entered her confinement chamber. "It is now said that the delivery may be protracted until the end of next month, and perhaps to that of September", wrote the Venetian ambassador. He noticed that "all persons seem to have resigned themselves to bide that time, which will never have been too late or wearisome should it please God to render it in the end such as is desired and hoped for by all good men".[15]

In early August, however, the Queen was forced to admit that there was no child and ordered the entire household to move from Hampton Court to Oatlands Palace. By August, Hampton Court was in "very great need" of general cleansing, but the real reason behind the move was the fact that Mary was no longer with child. Giovanni Michieli wrote:

"The fact is, that the move has been made in order no longer to keep the people of England in suspense about this delivery, by the constant and public processions which were made, and by the Queen's remaining so many days in retirement, seriously to the prejudice of her subjects; as not only did she transact no business, but would scarcely allow herself to be seen by any but the ladies, who, in expectation of this childbirth, especially the gentlewomen and the chief female nobility, had flocked to the court from all parts of the kingdom in such very great number, all living at the cost of her Majesty, that with great difficulty could Hampton Court, although one of the largest palaces that can be seen here or elsewhere, contain them."[16]

With no child to serve, women returned to their homes in the countryside, and Mary could leave Hampton Court without causing a grand scandal, although damage to her reputation had already been done. Malicious rumours spread across the country. Some claimed that "this rumour of the Queen's conception was spread by policy" while others believed she was "deceived by a tympany [distension of the abdomen] or some other like disease". There were also those who believed the Queen was pregnant but had miscarried, and some even thought she was "bewitched".[17]

Today historians believe that she had either experienced a phantom pregnancy or suffered from prolactinoma, a tumour on the pituitary gland. Phantom pregnancy, or pseudocyesis, is a condition in which signs of pregnancy, such as swelling of the abdomen, cessation of menstruation and even emission of milk, are present despite the fact that there is no pregnancy. This condition is most likely to occur in women who desire to have a child or are under pressure to become pregnant. Phantom pregnancy seems the most likely explanation since Mary had suffered "from menstruous retention and suffocation of the matrix" since puberty and had experienced painful and erratic periods for years.[18] When she was fifteen, she was "very ill from what the physicians call 'the mother'".[19] Mary could have easily mistaken the lack of menstruation with pregnancy, and a tumour that grew inside her belly certainly contributed to her misguided belief that she was with child.

King Philip, humiliated by Mary's phantom pregnancy, decided not to delay his departure from England any longer. Philip left the distraught Mary in August 1555, and when he met with his father, he told him plainly that "there is no hope of fruit from the English marriage".[20]

Sadly, the phantom pregnancy Mary experienced in 1555 wasn't her only humiliation. In 1557, Philip returned, and by the time he left England for the second and last time, she believed she was pregnant again. "They say it is quite certain that she is pregnant, although she tries to keep it a secret", wrote Pedro de Ocaña, a Spanish diplomat who had an audience with Mary on 25 February 1558.[21] In December 1557, Mary herself confirmed the news when she sent her courier to Philip to inform him that she reckoned herself to be around seven months pregnant. Yet she carefully avoided confirming her condition to her courtiers, although they suspected she was with child. Pedro de Ocaña speculated that Mary would give birth in late February or in early March and insisted he learned it from her trusted lady-in-waiting Susan Clarencius, who was present during the audience. The Venetian ambassador at Philip's court reported:

"The Count de Feria tells me that his going to England is for several causes, the first to congratulate the Queen on the advice given by her these Christmas holidays to his Majesty of her being pregnant, which thing she has chosen to keep secret until now, a period of seven months, in order to be quite sure of the fact, lest the like should happen as last time, when this thing was published all over the world, and then did not prove true, whereas now, having very sure signs of it, she willed to acquaint his Majesty with the circumstance."[22]

The Queen believed she would give birth in March and summoned her hated half sister, Elizabeth to court, as she had three years earlier, to witness her triumph. Elizabeth arrived on 28 February accompanied by a "great company of lords and noblemen and noblewomen" and stayed at Somerset House.[23]

Gómez Suárez de Figueroa y Córdoba, Count de Feria, Philip's ambassador who came to England to keep the King informed about everyday occurrences at Mary's court, suspected that the Queen deluded herself that she was pregnant. "The one thing that matters to her is that your Majesty should come hither", de Feria wrote, "and it seems to me she is making herself believe that she is with child, although she does not own up to it".[24] This time Mary decided to keep her pregnancy a secret and shared the news only with those whom she trusted. For some unknown reason, perhaps when she heard rumours that the Queen was mistaken again, Elizabeth left London on 4 March 1558, accompanied by her large retinue. The next time she would return to London would be as Queen of England.

On 30 March 1558, Mary, "thinking myself to be with child", made her last will. The document was composed in anticipation of the birth of her heir. Childbirth was a risky business, and Mary was forty-two. Her grandmother and two stepmothers had perished as a result of childbed fever, and they had been younger than Mary. The Queen, "foreseeing the great danger which by God's ordinance remain to all women in their travail of children", made necessary provisions for the succession. Her crown was to devolve "unto the heirs, issue and fruit of my body, according to the laws of this realm".[25]

At the end of April, Mary knew that she had never been pregnant. "She now realises that her pregnancy has come to nothing", de Feria informed Philip on 1 May 1558. "She is somewhat better than she was a few days ago, but she sleeps badly, is weak and suffers from melancholy", he added further.[26] Mary was now severely depressed and mortally ill.

On 17 May 1558, Mary moved from Greenwich to St James's Palace, visiting Cardinal Pole at Lambeth on her way "in one of the heaviest rain storms ever seen". "She is suffering from her usual ailments", de Feria observed in a detailed despatch.[27] In early June, he reported to Philip that Mary was "worse than usual". The Queen wrote to her husband on a regular basis, and when several days elapsed and Philip received no letters from Mary, he grew worried.

"I am sending the present courier to ask you to inform the Queen that I am well and to give me news of her health", he wrote to de Feria. "She has not written to me for some days past, and I cannot help being anxious."[28] At the end of June, it appeared that Mary rallied. "The Queen is better than she has been recently", de Feria informed Philip after three weeks of hiatus.[29]

In late August 1558, however, the Queen became feverish and took to her bed at St James's Palace. In a report to Philip, Reginald Pole wrote that "the physicians were and are of the opinion that through this malady she will obtain relief from her habitual indisposition". Pole also wrote that:

"During her malady the Queen did not fail to take the greatest care of herself, following the advice of the physicians; and by continuing to do so it is hoped she will recover, and daily more and more establish her health; a result to which nothing can contribute more than to receive frequent good news of his Majesty."[30]

As September turned to October, however, it became clear that Mary was dying. On 28 October 1558, she added a codicil to her last will, acknowledging the fact that she was dying without direct heirs, having "no fruit nor heir of my body". Still, she nourished the hope that she would be blessed with children if she survived, attesting that it lay in God's power "whether I shall have any [children] or no".[31] As she lay dying in her bedchamber, surrounded by her faithful ladies-in-waiting, the Queen was pressured to name Elizabeth as her successor. Mary's advisors feared that if she failed to name Elizabeth as the next Queen, a civil war would break out. The threat of another War of the Roses, with various claimants bickering over the crown, loomed large over England as the Queen struggled to accept the inevitable. In the codicil to her will, she came close to naming Elizabeth as her heiress:

"If it shall please Almighty God to call me to his mercy out of this transitory life without issue and heir of my body lawfully begotten, then I most instantly per viscera misericordiae Dei [by the tender mercy of our God], require my next heir and successor, by the laws and statutes of this realm . . ."[32]

Still, Mary could not bring herself to name Elizabeth by name, but it was clear to everyone that the Queen meant her sister when she appointed her heir "by the laws and statutes of this realm". Still, that was not enough: it was of utmost importance for Mary to name Elizabeth; there could be no ambiguity about her last will. Mary despised Elizabeth "because of her heretical opinions, illegitimacy and characteristics in which she resembled her mother".[33] She also confided to her ladies-in-waiting that she felt Elizabeth wasn't her real sister but a product of Anne Boleyn's liaison with Mark Smeaton, the musician executed in 1536.

On 6 November, the Queen received a delegation of her chief councillors in her bedchamber, urging her "to make certain declarations in favour of the Lady Elizabeth concerning the succession". The Queen finally consented. Deep down in her heart, she knew Elizabeth was her sister and a Tudor. Mary herself had ascended to the throne in 1553 via the terms of Henry VIII's last will, overthrowing Lady Jane Grey, who had been appointed heiress by Edward VI. Now there was no other option but to honour Henry VIII's last will again.

Elizabeth was residing at Hatfield when Mary was dying at St James's Palace. She knew perfectly well that her accession was a matter of days, perhaps weeks away, having been informed of the Queen's deteriorating health by her friends at court. But Elizabeth wasn't sure if her sister would name her as heiress, and she began organising support. Just like Mary five years earlier, Elizabeth expected to fight for her crown if need be. For all she knew, Mary could appoint anyone whom she saw fit to wear their father's crown: Mary, Queen of Scots, Frances Grey or one of her two daughters, Margaret Douglas or one of her sons; it was all still in the air. Elizabeth soon left Hatfield for Brocket Hall, where she established her operational headquarters. If she could not take over peacefully, she would fight for her royal inheritance. In the end, however, the Queen recognised her as heiress.

Mary's health continued to deteriorate. Perhaps the vicious influenza epidemic that swept through England that autumn had weakened Mary's already fragile health. It's also possible that the symptoms Mary mistook for pregnancy were the manifestations of the illness that killed her, possibly an ovarian cyst. "Since the Queen's illness reached its climax, she has had some good intervals, and there have been days when she was free of the paroxysms from which she had suffered", de Feria informed Philip on 7 November.[34]

On 13 November, Mary's health worsened. There was no hope for her recovery, and "many personages of the kingdom flocked to the house of Milady Elizabeth, the crowd constantly increasing with great frequency".[35] Philip sent his own physician to treat Mary, but it was too late. In a letter to his sister Joanna, Dowager Princess of Portugal, Philip wrote:

"The Queen, my wife, has been ill; and although she has recovered somewhat, her infirmities are such that grave fears must be entertained on her score, as a physician I sent to her with Count Feria writes to me. All these happenings are perplexing to me, and I am obliged to ponder much on the government to be provided for the Low Countries, and also on what I must do in England, in the event either of the Queen's survival or of her death, for these are questions of the greatest importance, on which the welfare of my realms depends. I will say nothing of my own peace and quiet, which matters little in this connexion."[36]

Drifting in and out of consciousness, Mary talked to her maid, Jane Dormer. The Queen knew that Philip's ambassador, the Count de Feria, intended to marry Jane. Mary wanted to attend their wedding, but it was also her great wish to have Philip by her side, so she kept delaying their nuptials, waiting for her husband's arrival. As she lay dying, it occurred to Mary that she was the reason why Mistress Dormer was not married yet. Mary told Jane that "she would have been glad to have seen her marriage effected in her days; but God Almighty would otherwise dispose, and being sick and the King absent, she was not in case to do what she would".[37] In her last moments, the Queen did not think about herself, but about the women who had dedicated their lives to her service:

"She comforted those of them that grieved about her; she told them what good dreams she had, seeing many little children like angels play before her, singing pleasing notes, giving her more than earthly comfort; and thus persuaded all, ever to have the holy fear of God before their eyes, which would free them from all evil, and be a curb to all temptation. She asked them to think that whatsoever came to them was by God's permission; and ever to have confidence that He would in mercy turn all to the best."[38]

During her last hours, Mary heard Mass in her bedchamber. Jane Dormer affirmed that the Queen "heard it with so good attention, zeal, and devotion" and retained "the quickness of her senses and memory".[39] Yet the Count de Feria informed Philip that the Queen was "unconscious most of the time since I arrived [9 November]".[40] The Queen received extreme unction on 15 November, and the next day her last will was read out in the presence of her household, although Mary was unconscious at the time.

News of Mary's mortal illness spread throughout Europe like wildfire. Michiel Surian, Venetian ambassador at Philip's court, heard that "her malady is evidently incurable, and will end her life sooner or later, according to the increase or decrease of her mental anxieties, which harass her more than the disease, however dangerous it may be".[41] Indeed, Mary had suffered from severe anxiety and depression since she was a teenager. Her fragile mental state was further aggravated by the fact that she knew Elizabeth was to succeed her. But the factor that contributed the most to her demise was Philip's absence, and it was widely reported that she missed him dearly and despaired that he was not by her side during her last days.

The Queen breathed her last on 17 November 1558 at seven o'clock in the morning. She slipped so peacefully away that only her physician noticed that she was dead; others thought she was sleeping. It was reported that Mary "made her passage so tranquilly that had not a physician remarked it on its commencement, all the other persons present would have thought her better, and that she would fain sleep".[42]

At Hatfield, Elizabeth awaited news from court. She was cautious not to take any steps towards her recognition as Queen until she was absolutely sure that Mary was dead. If she proclaimed herself Queen while Mary was still alive, or worse, after the Queen recovered, it could be used against Elizabeth and construed as treason. To avoid such a situation, she secretly employed her trusted servant, Sir Nicholas Throckmorton, to bring her the news of Mary's passing as soon as it occurred. Elizabeth bade him "to hasten to the palace and request one of the ladies of the bedchamber, who was in her confidence, if the Queen were really dead, to send her, as a token, the black enamelled ring which Her Majesty wore night and day".[43]

In her last moments, the Queen was surrounded by faithful ladies-in-waiting who had been part of her household before her accession. Susan Clarencius had served Mary since her teenaged years and was "a woman respected and beloved by the Queen".[44] Others, like Frideswide Strelley, Barbara Hawke, Eleanor Kempe and Jane Dormer were also among the most trusted women of the Queen's bedchamber. One of them slipped the ring from Mary's dead hand and gave it to Throckmorton.

Before Mary's body was cold, Throckmorton galloped at full speed from St James's Palace to Hatfield. When he arrived, however, he learned that members of the Privy Council had reached Elizabeth before him, and he regretfully recorded in his biographical poem that "my news was stale".[45] According to a legend recorded seventy years later, Mary's councillors approached Elizabeth as she walked in the nearby park. Swathed in fur to ward off the autumn chill, Elizabeth stood beneath an oak tree when the councillors knelt before her, informing her that the Queen, her royal sister, was dead. Overcome by emotion, Elizabeth knelt on the grass, turned her gaze towards heaven and quoted from Psalm 118, verse 23: "This is the Lord's doing and it is marvellous in our eyes." It was an apt quotation, as the previous verse read: "The same stone which the builders refused is become the headstone in the corner." It seemed unbelievable that the daughter of an executed adulteress, proclaimed illegitimate by her father and almost disinherited by her sister, was now Queen. Finally, after five years of living in constant fear of Mary, Elizabeth could breathe a sigh of relief. She was, at last, Queen.

NOTES

[1] Queen Mary I, attributed to Lucas Horenbout (or Hornebolte) watercolour on vellum, circa 1525, NPG 6453 https://www.npg.org.uk/collections/search/portrait/mw09583/Queen-Mary-I
[2] J. A. Froude, *Mary Tudor*, p. 84.
[3] *Calendar of State Papers, Spain,* Volume 13, n. 37.
[4] *Calendar of State Papers, Venice,* Volume 5, n. 934.
[5] *Calendar of State Papers Relating To English Affairs in the Archives of Venice,* Volume 6, n. 884.

---

[6] *Calendar of State Papers, Spain,* Volume 13, n. 30.
[7] Ibid., n. 130.
[8] Ibid., n. 178.
[9] Ibid., n. 204.
[10] *Calendar of State Papers, Venice,* Volume 6, n. 124.
[11] *Calendar of State Papers, Spain,* Volume 13, n. 216.
[12] *Calendar of State Papers, Venice,* Volume 6, n. 116.
[13] Ibid., n. 146.
[14] *Calendar of State Papers, Spain,* Volume 13, n. 216.
[15] *Calendar of State Papers, Venice,* Volume 6, n. 165.
[16] Ibid., n. 174.
[17] Sylvia Barbara Soberton, *Great Ladies*, p. 208.
[18] *Calendar of State Papers, Venice,* Volume 6, 1555-1558, n. 884.
[19] Ibid., n. 664.
[20] *Calendar of State Papers, Spain,* Volume 13, n. 249.
[21] Sylvia Barbara Soberton, *Great Ladies*, p. 210.
[22] *Calendar of State Papers, Venice,* Volume 6, 1555-1558 n. 1142.
[23] *The Diary of Henry Machyn,* pp. 166-167.
[24] *Calendar of State Papers, Spain,* Volume 13, 1554-1558., n. 413.
[25] David Loades, *Mary Tudor*, p. 370.
[26] *Calendar of State Papers, Spain,* Volume 13, n. 425.
[27] Ibid., n. 435.
[28] Ibid., n. 450.
[29] Ibid., n. 451.
[30] *Calendar of State Papers, Venice,* Volume 6, 1555-1558 n. 1264.
[31] David Loades, *Mary Tudor*, p. 381.
[32] Ibid., pp. 381-382.
[33] *Calendar of State Papers, Spain,* Volume 11, 28 November 1553.
[34] *Calendar of State Papers, Spain,* Volume 13, 1554-1558., n. 498.
[35] *Calendar of State Papers, Venice,* Volume 6, 1555-1558 n. 1285.
[36] *Calendar of State Papers, Spain,* Volume 13, 1554-1558., n. 502.
[37] Henry Clifford, *The Life of Jane Dormer, Duchess of Feria*, p. 71.
[38] Ibid., p. 70.
[39] Ibid., p. 71.
[40] *Calendar of State Papers, Spain (Simancas),* Volume 1, 1558-1567, n.1.
[41] *Calendar of State Papers, Venice,* Volume 6, 1555-1558 n. 1287.
[42] Ibid.
[43] Agnes Strickland, *Lives of the Queens of England: From the Norman Conquest*, Volumes 6-7, p. 103.
[44] Henry Clifford, *The Life of Jane Dormer, Duchess of Feria*, p. 109.
[45] Agnes Strickland, op. cit.

CHAPTER 21: "THIS WOMAN IS UNHEALTHY"

Judging from the eloquent speech she gave during her first Parliament in February 1559, Queen Elizabeth intended never to marry: "And in the end this shall be for me sufficient, that a marble stone shall declare that a Queen, having reigned such a time, lived and died a virgin." No one took her resolve seriously, however, and it was not until the 1580s that Elizabeth successfully established herself as England's iconic Virgin Queen. In the same speech in 1559, Elizabeth firmly rebuffed her councillors' efforts to name her successor in the event of her death without issue. Recalling her own experience during Mary's reign, Elizabeth refused to name such a person for fear that rebellions would invoke his or her name. "I stood in danger of my life, my sister was so incensed against me", she said with bitterness, adding that she would never name a successor during her lifetime.[1]

Elizabeth's childhood friend Robert Dudley would recall many years later in a conversation with the French ambassador that Elizabeth had first made the decision never to marry when she was a child:

"Then speaking less guardedly he [Dudley] told me that his true opinion was that she [Elizabeth] would never marry. To convince me he added that he considered that he knew her Majesty as well as or better than anyone else of her close acquaintance, for they had first become friends before she was eight years old [c. 1541]. Both then and later (when she was old enough to marry) she said she never wished to do so."[2]

Elizabeth had resisted her half sister's attempts to marry her to Philibert of Savoy. In 1556, she "said plainly that she will not marry, even were they to give her the King's son [Don Carlos], or find any other greater Prince."[3] Marriage with a Habsburg prince was as much a political as a personal slight for Elizabeth, for she knew that a union with a candidate named by Mary and Philip would forever tie her to Habsburg interests, and she had no intention of becoming their puppet. The Savoy match was dropped, as Queen Mary thought it beneath her station to offer such a great prince to her illegitimate half sister.

Still, as sister of the childless Queen of England, Elizabeth was a glittering marriage prospect. When in 1558 an embassy arrived from Gustavus Vasa of Sweden soliciting Elizabeth's hand for his heir, Eric, Elizabeth refused again. The Swedish ambassador didn't request an audience with Queen Mary and went to see Elizabeth before seeking Mary's permission. Yet Elizabeth prudently expressed her wish not to marry, informing the Queen that "I so well like this [single] estate, as I persuade myself there is not any kind of life comparable unto it".[4] "Now that the Lady Elizabeth has answered that she does not wish to marry, the Queen has calmed down; but she takes a most passionate interest in the affair", wrote ambassador de Feria.[5]

Elizabeth's refusal to countenance marriage may have been rooted in the overall state of her health, as she was never considered a robust or healthy individual. On her accession, the general consensus was that she would not live long, and prophecies circulated saying that "she will reign a very short time".[6] During her half sister's reign, Elizabeth suffered from dropsy, a condition characterised by an excess of watery fluid collecting in the cavities or tissues of the body. Her face, arms and hands were swollen, and this was, according to the physician who treated her at the time, because Elizabeth's body was "replenished with many cold and waterish humours".[7] She was shortsighted, prone to headaches and very thin. In 1561, dropsy returned, as Elizabeth started "to swell extraordinarily".[8] "To all appearance she is falling away, and is extremely thin and the colour of a corpse", wrote the Spanish ambassador.[9]

Elizabeth's decision to shun matrimony met with the disapproval of her councillors and subjects alike. When she fell ill of smallpox in October 1562 and brushed with death, Elizabeth's councillors petitioned her again concerning "my marriage and my successor". In April 1563, Elizabeth replied with a formal statement, invoking memories from Mary's time as Queen:

"Princes cannot like their own children, those that should succeed them . . . so long as I live, I shall be Queen of England; when I am dead, they shall succeed me that has most right . . . I know the inconstancy of the people of England, how they ever mislike the present government and have their eyes fixed upon that person that is next to succeed . . . I have good experience of myself in my sister's time how desirous men were that I should be in [her] place, and earnest to set me up [on the throne]."[10]

Why Elizabeth chose never to marry remains one of her life's most mysterious aspects. She lived in a patriarchal society where aristocratic women's only aspiration, other than carving out successful careers as ladies-in-waiting, was to marry well and produce a large brood of children to carry their legacy into the next generation. Only Elizabeth knew why she chose a single life. She certainly didn't like the idea of a woman becoming her husband's property and was loath to share her throne with a husband. There may have been other reasons as well. Elizabeth once declared that "for her part she hated the idea of marriage every day more, for reasons which she would not divulge to a twin soul, if she had one, much less to a living creature".[11] William Camden, Elizabeth's first biographer, claimed that:

"The perils by conception and childbearing, objected by the physicians and her gentlewomen for some private reasons, did many times run in her mind, and very much deter her from thoughts of marrying."[12]

What these "private reasons" were remains unknown. Historians over the centuries tried to figure out what kind of physical infirmity Elizabeth had that prevented her from marrying and having children. In the nineteenth century, the famous writer Bram Stoker proposed that the real Elizabeth died in 1542 and a local boy took her place so as not to displease Henry VIII. The

"Bisley Boy" theory, although rejected by academic historians, attracts the attention of conspiracy theorists.[13]

In recent years, Michael Bloch suggested that Elizabeth suffered from androgen insensitivity syndrome (AIS). People born with this condition have XY male chromosomes but develop outwardly as female because their bodies don't produce enough male hormones. People affected with this syndrome have no ovaries, so conception is impossible, the womb is malformed and the vagina shallow, making penetration painful if not downright impossible. Tall and slender, people with AIS tend to have dominant personalities. It seems unlikely that Elizabeth suffered from AIS, however. She wouldn't menstruate without ovaries, and her contemporaries referred to her irregular menstruations. Even Elizabeth's enemy Mary, Queen of Scots didn't doubt that although Elizabeth was unlike other women in terms of her intimate health, she menstruated, saying in 1584 that "without doubt, as you was [sic] coming to lose your menses, you would die soon".[14] Ben Johnson, playwright and poet, suggested that Elizabeth "had a membrane on her which made her incapable of man, though for her delight she tried many".[15] The Queen's godson Sir John Harrington also noted that "In mind, she hath ever had an aversion and (as many think) in body some indisposition to the act of marriage".[16]

Many contemporaries suggested that Elizabeth was physically unable to bear children. Foreign ambassadors often wrote about the Queen's intimate health, repeating rumours that "this woman is unhealthy, and it is believed certain that she will not have children".[17] Like her half sister, Mary, Elizabeth suffered from erratic periods caused by hormonal imbalance. William Camden recorded that Dr Robert Huicke, the Queen's physician, believed Elizabeth should never marry because of her "womanish impotency", incurring the wrath of her councillors.[18] One of Elizabeth's ladies-in-waiting, Elizabeth Countess of Shrewsbury, told the disgruntled Mary, Queen of Scots that Elizabeth "was not as all other women are" and for this reason "it was folly" to push for the match with the Duke of Anjou "because it could never be consummated".[19]

Elizabeth often experienced violent stomach pains and bouts of weeping and rage. The Tudors had no knowledge of hormones, but they connected the mental health of women with irregular menstruations. Elizabeth hardly ever had "purgation proper to all women", as menstruation was described by one foreign ambassador, and in 1572 it was reported that she was "troubled with a spice or show of Mother". The words "mother" and "matrix" described the womb or uterus and were understood to mean bouts of "fits", which in Elizabeth's case lasted "not above a quarter of an hour".[20] These "fits" were probably caused by cramps during painful menstruations. It is thus reasonable to assume that Elizabeth suffered from dysmenorrhea—painful periods. Ambassadors and the Queen's correspondents often referred to her "wonted pangs", likely meaning uterine cramps.[21] Additionally, she "was subject to a failure [palpitation] of the heart which returned every month", a condition today closely associated with premenstrual dysphoric disorder (PMDD).[22]

In 1603, Edward Jorden published his *Briefe Discourse of a Disease Called the Suffocation of the Mother*, treating about a natural "disease" that he called "Passio Hysterica" or the "Suffocation of the Mother". The word "mother" meant womb or uterus. In keeping with the Hippocratic belief, Jorden argued that virgins were most prone to this disease because they were deprived of sexual intercourse. The lack of sexual activity, Jorden argued, created "a congestion of humours" and corruption around the womb. Like Hippocrates before him, Jorden believed the womb was a living organism that moved around the body, pressuring vital organs and causing symptoms such as "frenzies, convulsions, hiccups, laughing, singing, weeping and crying".[23]

Elizabeth experienced many outbursts of uncontrollable rage. In 1569, for instance, she was so angry at her kinsman the Duke of Norfolk that she "fainted, and they ran for vinegar and other remedies to revive her".[24] Her temper tantrums were notorious. Francis Knollys reminded his wife, Katherine, who was Elizabeth's kinswoman and favourite, that "for the outward love that her Majesty bears you, she makes you often weep for unkindness to the great danger of your health".[25] Elizabeth often slapped her ladies and lashed out at them. Bess of Hardwick confided in the captive Mary, Queen of Scots how Elizabeth had broken one of her maids' fingers and blamed the incident on a falling candelabra.[26] The maid, Mary Shelton, secretly married in 1574 and received "blows and evil words" from the Queen on that account.[27] Also, on one occasion Elizabeth dealt "a great blow with a knife upon the hand of a lady" who served her at the table.[28] Bess told Mary, Queen of Scots that she would never return to court to attend Elizabeth because she was afraid of her when she was in a rage.

Vigorous sexual intercourse was believed to cure women and soothe their nerves. William Cecil, the Queen's closest adviser, argued that marriage could protect the Queen from illness that usually afflicted women who abstained from sex. He said that by eschewing matrimony, "her Majesty's own person shall daily be subject to such dolours and infirmities as all physicians do usually impute to womankind for lack of marriage".[29] Elizabeth was forty-six years at the time and deep in marriage negotiations with Francis of Valois, Duke of Anjou. William Cecil, Lord Burghley, interviewed the Queen's ladies and physicians to ascertain whether at such an age she was still capable of having children and scribbled his observations in the following memorandum:

"Considering the proportion of her body, having no impediment of smallness in stature, of largeness in body, nor no sickness nor lack of natural functions in those things that properly belong to the procreation of children, but contrariwise by judgment of physicians that know her estate in those things, and by opinion of women, being more acquainted with Her Majesty's body in such things as properly appertain, to show probability of her aptness to have children, even at this day."[30]

Cecil invoked the example of the late Margaret of France, Duchess of Savoy, "who being of more years when she was married than her Majesty is and a woman of sallow and melancholy complexion and in all respects inferior to Her Majesty". Here Cecil was wrong in his calculations because the Duchess of Savoy gave birth to her first and only son at the age of thirty-eight, not forty-six. Yet Cecil was optimistic about Elizabeth's childbearing potential, estimating that the Queen would have some five or six fertile years before menopause would set in:

"It is therefore greatly to be hoped that her Majesty, a person of most pure complexion, of the largest and goodliest stature of well-shaped women, with all limbs set and proportioned in the best sort, and one whom in the sight of all men nature cannot amend her shape in any part to make her more likely to conceive and bear children without peril, may with safety or at the least with as little peril as any other, conceive . . ."[31]

In 1580, Anjou became less ardent in his pursuit of Elizabeth when "he called to mind the advanced age and repulsive physical nature of the Queen, she being, in addition to her other ailments, half consumptive".[32] In the end, the marriage negotiations came to nothing, and the Queen's childbearing years were soon past.

Deteriorating health, fading beauty and the deaths of her loved ones took their toll on Elizabeth. As she grew older, the Queen was becoming ever more eccentric and self-obsessed. She liked to encourage foreign ambassadors into complimenting her appearance. "Whenever anyone speaks of her beauty she says that she was never beautiful", observed the French ambassador in 1597, adding, "Nevertheless, she speaks of her beauty as often as she can".[33] Bess of Hardwick told Mary, Queen of Scots that Elizabeth was "vain, and had as good an opinion of her beauty, as if she were some goddess of the sky". The Queen's women knew that Elizabeth "took so great a pleasure in flatteries beyond all reason" and told her that they could not look directly at her face because "it shone like the sun". This, of course, was a hidden mockery. Bess also recounted how her daughter could not cease to "laugh up her sleeve" at the old Queen. Bess herself was no better; she and her friend Margaret Douglas, Countess of Lennox, could not look at each other while in the Queen's presence "for fear of bursting into gales of laughter".[34]

Elizabeth frequently elicited affirmations of her good looks and made sure that her wrinkled face, ravaged by poisonous makeup, was carefully concealed behind what one historian called "the mask of youth".[35] Painters and miniaturists were forbidden to show the real likeness of the Queen, depicting her instead as the iconic, changeless and radiant Virgin Queen. Elizabeth hated posing for portraits, and "the natural representation of Her Majesty" was forbidden from being painted directly from life. Instead, one officially approved face pattern was produced and inserted into all subsequent portraits.[36] Posing for a portrait took up to three or four hours if the artist was skilled in his craft; the Queen preferred her ladies-in-waiting to be dressed and styled, pretending to be her, instead of sitting in one pose for hours on end. By the time she reached her sixties, Elizabeth was bald, having only wisps of her natural grey hair hanging to her shoulders when she was not wearing elaborate wigs. The skin on her wrinkled face, often painted with a toxic mixture of white lead and vinegar, was dry and deathly pale.

Elizabeth was terribly afraid of the procedure of tooth extraction since it was painful and did not guarantee a successful outcome, and she suffered from toothache on a regular basis. In 1577, for instance, it was reported that "the Queen was in some part of this year under excessive anguish by pains of her teeth insomuch that she took no rest for divers nights, and endured very great torment night and day".[37] In 1597, the French ambassador Andre Hurault, Sieur de Maisse, recorded that "her teeth are very yellow and unequal, compared with what they were formerly, so they say, and on the left side less than on the right. Many of them are missing so that one cannot understand her easily when she speaks quickly".[38]

Elizabeth's penchant for sweets contributed to her problem with toothache. She also gained considerable weight over the years. In 1581, one of her tailors was paid for altering and enlarging some items of clothing, including thirty pairs of bodices, and in 1596 the Venetian ambassador remarked that the Queen was "very strongly built".[39] These descriptions are borne out by several miniatures painted by the Queen's favourite court painter, Nicholas Hilliard, who depicted her with a fuller face and incipient double chin.

Elizabeth enjoyed showing herself off in her finest gowns, jewel-encrusted wigs and loaded with heavy necklaces made of large pearls and gemstones. Elizabeth, who retained her "vigorous disposition", often appeared grotesque in her voluminous gowns and excessive ornaments.[40] She was loath to acknowledge that she grew older and weaker. "Age in itself is a sickness", she once mused in a conversation with her much-favoured godson John Harrington.[41] Women, who knew what was happening behind closed doors, often ridiculed and poked fun at their royal mistress. They often laughed at Elizabeth for "trying to play the part of a woman still young".[42] Indeed, Elizabeth tried to pretend that she was young and attractive and often danced, walked tirelessly in her gardens and stomped her feet at bad news.

As Elizabeth aged, the question of who would succeed England's Virgin Queen was asked more frequently than ever. King James VI of Scotland, son of the executed Mary, Queen of Scots, was the most likely successor. Elizabeth's courtiers "adored him as the rising sun, and neglected her as being now ready to set".[43] Just like her half sister, Mary, Elizabeth was buried alive by her fickle courtiers, who were now weary of the Virgin Queen's longevity and flocked to James's side. Knowing the constant speculation upon her mortality, Elizabeth would many times observe wryly that she was "mortua non sepulta", dead but not yet buried. Yet, as if out of spite, she tried to prove to her courtiers that she was not ready to satisfy them and drop dead. The physical activity she liked so much kept her fit, and she remained agile until the end. In 1597, when she was sixty-four, the French ambassador observed that it was "a strange thing to see how lively she is in body and mind, and nimble in everything she does".[44] Five years later a visitor to Oatlands Palace saw her "walking as freely as if she had been only eighteen years old".[45] By that time she danced rarely, but in February 1600 she danced energetically to "show that she is not so old as some would have her".[46] She rode on horseback and hunted into her late sixties, but she often rested for two days after an hour in the saddle. Elizabeth could not cheat time; she was getting older, and the younger generation of courtiers was looking at her with pity rather than admiration.

NOTES

[1] Maria Perry, *The Word of a Prince*, p. 100.
[2] Simon Adams, *Leicester and the Court: Essays on Elizabethan Politics*, p. 139.
[3] *Calendar of State Papers, Venice,* Volume 6, n. 466.
[4] Frank A. Mumby, *The Girlhood of Queen Elizabeth*, p. 237.
[5] *Calendar of State Papers, Spain,* Volume 13, 1554-1558., n. 425.
[6] Frederick Chamberlin, *The Private Character of Queen Elizabeth,* p. 49.
[7] Ibid., p. 47.
[8] *Calendar of State Papers, Spain (Simancas),* Volume 1, 1558-1567, n. 139.
[9] Ibid.
[10] Felix Pryor (ed.), *Elizabeth I: Her Life in Letters*, p. 43.
[11] *Calendar of State Papers, Spain (Simancas),* Volume 3, n. 189.
[12] Carole Levin, *The Heart and Stomach of a King: Elizabeth I and the Politics of Sex and Power*, p. 86.
[13] Bram Stoker, *Famous Impostors*, pp. 283-345.
[14] Hugh Campbell (ed.), *The Love Letters of Mary, Queen of Scots*, p. 3.
[15] Alison Weir, *Elizabeth the Queen*, p. 49.
[16] Ibid., p. 48.

[17] *Calendar of State Papers, Spain (Simancas),* Volume 1, *1558-1567,* n. 122.

[18] William Camden, *The History of the Most Renowned and Victorious Princess Elizabeth*, Book 1, p. 83.

[19] Hugh Campbell (ed.), *The Love Letters of Mary, Queen of Scots*, p. 2.

[20] Frederick Chamberlin, *The Private Character of Queen Elizabeth,* p. 62.

[21] Ibid., p. 60.

[22] Ibid., p. 67.

[23] Edward Jorden, *A Briefe Discourse of a Disease Called the Suffocation of the Mother*, p. 17.

[24] Frederick Chamberlin, *The Private Character of Queen Elizabeth,* p. 58.

[25] Susan Doran, *Elizabeth & Her Circle*, p. 213.

[26] Hugh Campbell (ed.), *The Love Letters of Mary, Queen of Scots*, p. 3.

[27] *The Manuscripts of His Grace the Duke of Rutland, G.C.B., Preserved at Belvoir Castle,* Volume 1, p. 107.

[28] Hugh Campbell, op. cit.

[29] Susan Doran, *Monarchy and Matrimony: The Courtships of Elizabeth I,* p. 197.

[30] *HMC, Salisbury,* Volume 9, Part 2, p. 240.

[31] Ibid.

[32] *Calendar of State Papers and Manuscripts Relating to English Affairs Existing in the Archives and Collections of Venice*, Volume 7, p. xxxii.

[33] Anna Riehl, *The Face of Queenship*, p. 46.

[34] Hugh Campbell (ed.), *The Love Letters of Mary, Queen of Scots*, p. 2.

[35] Roy Strong, *Nicholas Hilliard*, pp. 14-19 and 21-6, and *Artists of the Tudor Court*, pp. 9-13 and 126-32.

[36] George Lillie Craik, *The Pictorial History of England*, p. 550.

[37] Frederick Chamberlin, *The Private Character of Queen Elizabeth*, p. 67.

[38] Janet Arnold, *Queen Elizabeth's Wardrobe Unlock'd*, p. 8.

[39] Ibid., p. 1.

[40] Ibid., p. 10.

[41] Donna B. Hamilton, *Shakespeare and the Politics of Protestant England,* p. 87.

[42] Tracy Borman, *Elizabeth's Women*, p. 376.

[43] William Camden, *The History of the Most Renowned and Victorious Princess Elizabeth*, p. 659.

[44] Louis Montrose, *The Subject of Elizabeth: Authority, Gender, and Representation*, p. 238.

[45] Ibid.
[46] Carolly Erickson, *The First Elizabeth*, p. 403.

Chapter 22: "Naughty woman of her body"

Elizabeth I never married and produced no children, but during her long reign rumours about her alleged pregnancies and illegitimate children regularly circulated in England and abroad. In the early seventeenth century, Jane Dormer, Duchess of Feria, dictated her memoir to her English secretary, Henry Clifford. By that time, Queen Elizabeth was dead after ruling England successfully for forty-five years. Jane, a former servant of Queen Mary Tudor, wasn't convinced by Elizabeth's image of a Virgin Queen and published a series of denigrating stories about her reputation, attacking Elizabeth's chastity.

In Jane's view, Elizabeth was "proud and disdainful". She cited evidence from one of Elizabeth's servants, who related to her Elizabeth's "scornful behaviour, which much blemished the handsomeness and beauty of her person". It was Jane who suggested that a young noblewoman who in 1548 had secretly given birth to an illegitimate child was actually Elizabeth and the child was Thomas Seymour's. She related how a midwife had secretly been called to attend the birth and how the baby had been "miserably destroyed, but could not be discovered whose it was". Jane's story had an element of truth in it since during the time of Thomas Seymour's downfall in 1549, rumours circulated that Elizabeth was expecting his child, and there was also a report in London that a young noblewoman gave birth to baby who was murdered immediately after its birth. However, at the time Elizabeth vehemently denied that she was pregnant by Seymour and offered to appear at court to show off her slim figure.

Jane didn't directly say that the noblewoman in question was Elizabeth, but she strongly implied she was since "there was a muttering of the Admiral and this lady, who was then between fifteen and sixteen years of age". "If it were so, it was the judgment of God upon the Admiral", Jane recorded self-righteously, "and upon her, to make her ever after incapable of children".[1] It has been recently suggested that the woman who secretly gave birth to her lover's child may have been none other than Anne Hungerford, Jane Dormer's beloved sister.[2]

Yet Jane's story seems far-fetched and was clearly dictated with the aim of destroying Elizabeth's reputation. No respectable midwife would kill a healthy newborn child, this being a gross violation of an oath midwives took, promising they would "not destroy the child born of any woman".[3]

There is no evidence that Elizabeth had children, although rumours of illicit pregnancies and a host of lovers followed in her wake because she was an unmarried, powerful woman. Early in her reign, Elizabeth gave rise to such rumours because she favoured her childhood sweetheart, Robert Dudley, who served as her Master of the Horse. In April 1559, the Count de Feria remarked: "During the last few days Lord Robert has come so much into favour that he does whatever he likes with affairs and it is even said that her Majesty visits him in his chamber day and night".[4] The scandal reached vast proportions, not only because Elizabeth invited gossip by spending private hours with Dudley in her chambers but also because Robert was a married man. Son of her sister's sworn enemy, Robert was said to have been the Queen's lover. When Elizabeth complained to the Spanish ambassador about slanderous rumours touching their relationship, she marvelled how anyone could entertain any doubts of her moral purity since "my life is in the open and I have so many witnesses that I cannot understand how so bad a judgment can have been formed of me".[5]

Whether she was sleeping with Robert Dudley remains speculative, but Elizabeth's statement when she believed she was dying may be taken as confirmation that she was chaste and never had sexual relations with Robert. In October 1562, Elizabeth fell ill with smallpox. She wanted Dudley to become Lord Protector with an annual salary of £20,000. To convince her councillors to agree to this, "the Queen protested at the time that although she loved and had always loved Lord Robert dearly, as God was her witness, nothing improper had ever passed between them".[6] Considering that Elizabeth believed to have been dying of smallpox, it is unlikely that she was lying. At the same time, she granted an annual salary of £500 to Robert Dudley's groom of the chamber, Tamworth. Tamworth often slept in Robert's bedchamber and accompanied him in his most private moments. Was Elizabeth rewarding him for keeping secret the truth of her private relations with Dudley? It remains a tantalising possibility.

Robert Dudley, whom Elizabeth rewarded with the earldom of Leicester in 1564, came very close to marrying her. Yet his reputation was much tarnished when his first wife was found dead at the bottom of a staircase. Malicious tongues affirmed that Amy Dudley was killed to enable Robert to marry the Queen. The scandal that erupted sent shockwaves across Europe, and Elizabeth never married Robert, although he hoped against hope that she would. This was not to happen, but when Robert remarried in 1578, Elizabeth was furious, and although she welcomed him back at court after a brief period of banishment, she never forgave his wife, calling her "that She-Wolf".[7]

Still, Elizabeth's relationship with Dudley bred rumours that the two were lovers and had illegitimate children together. As early as 1559 the Count de Feria reported that although it was widely believed Elizabeth would have no children because of her unspecified infirmity, "there is no lack of people who say she has already had some, but of this I have seen no trace and do not believe it".[8]

In the 1560s and 1570s, when Elizabeth was still young enough for people to assume she was fertile, rumours of her pregnancies and illegitimate children were rife. Elizabeth's alleged pregnancies were usually linked to her annual summer progresses when she left the capital and visited the estates of her courtiers in the countryside. During the 1562 progress, one woman remarked that Elizabeth looked "very pale, like a woman out of childbed".[9] In 1564, Luis Roman, the former secretary of the Spanish ambassador, commented on Elizabeth's plans to visit the rebellious north of England: "Some say that she is pregnant and is going away to lie in".[10]

In 1572, the disgruntled Earl of Southampton told another prisoner in the Tower that "there was a privy stairs where the Queen and my Lord Leicester did meet, and if they had not used sorcery, there should have been young traitors 'ere now begotten".[11] In 1574, Spanish ambassador Antonio De Guaras heard that Elizabeth and Robert had a daughter.[12] In 1575, Nicholas Ormanetto, Bishop of Padua and papal Nuncio in Spain, heard that Elizabeth had a daughter and that Sir Henry Cobham, who was sent on an embassy to Spain, spread the rumour:

"I am assured that he has let it be known that the pretended Queen has a daughter, thirteen years of age, and that she would bestow her in marriage on someone acceptable to his Catholic Majesty. I have heard talk before of this daughter, but the English here say that they know nought of such a matter."[13]

Rumours of Elizabeth's illegitimate children didn't die down even when Elizabeth was in her late forties. In 1581, one Henry Hawkins claimed that Elizabeth had five children with Robert Dudley "and she never goethe in progress but to be delivered".[14] In 1590, Dionysia Derrick claimed that the Queen "had as many children as I, and that two of them were yet alive, one a man child and the other a maiden child, and the others were burned". Dudley, Derrick said, "wrapped them up in the embers which was in the chamber where they were born". About the same time Robert Gardner spread a similar report, saying that Elizabeth and Robert had four children together, "whereof three were daughters alive, and the fourth a son that was burnt".[15] Derrick and Gardner were both punished by standing in pillory for spreading calumnies about the Queen.

In 1598, Edward Fraunces tried to seduce one Elizabeth Baylie, informing her that Queen Elizabeth had two sons and a daughter with gentlemen of her court. If "the best in England", i.e. the Queen herself, engaged in unrestrained sexual activities, why wouldn't Baylie?[16]

While most of Elizabeth's illegitimate children are almost certainly products of her subjects' imaginations, there was one man who stepped forward and identified himself as the Virgin Queen's son. This man, Arthur Dudley, claimed to have been a lovechild of Elizabeth and Robert. He first appeared in the historical record in 1587, when he shipwrecked off the Spanish coast after many adventures overseas. According to his own testimony, Arthur was raised by Robert Southern, a former servant of Elizabeth's governess, Kat Ashley. On one occasion, Southern was summoned to Hampton Court:

"When he arrived, another lady of the Queen's court, named Harrington, asked him to obtain a nurse for a new-born child of a lady who had been so careless of her honour that, if it became known, it would bring great shame upon all the company, and would highly displease the Queen if she knew of it. The next morning, in a corridor leading to the Queen's private chamber, the child was given to the man, who was told that its name was Arthur. The man took the child, and gave it for some days to the wife of a miller of Moseley to suckle. He afterwards took it to a village near where he lived, twenty leagues from London, where the child remained until it was weaned. He then took it to his own house, and brought it up with his own children, in the place of one of his which had died in similar age."[17]

In May 1588, an English agent in Spain wrote that Arthur was "twenty-seven years of age, or thereabout".[18] That would place Arthur's birth c. 1561 and coincide with the rumours that in 1562 Elizabeth looked like "a woman out of childbed".[19] Whoever Arthur Dudley truly was, it's astonishing that his claims were investigated. The Queen was always upset by tales of her immorality. When, in the 1580s, Elizabeth entered marriage negotiations with Francis, Duke of Anjou, the French ambassador told her that she should marry him to save her reputation because many people believed that she and the duke had already slept together. Elizabeth said that she could disregard such a rumour, but the ambassador persisted, saying that she could quash rumours in her own country but not abroad, where tales of her immorality were rife. "She was extremely angry, and retorted that a clear and innocent conscience feared nothing".[20]

Did Elizabeth want to have children? Her half sister, Mary, seemed to have yearned to produce offspring to leave an heir behind and fulfil her own maternal instincts. But Elizabeth rarely spoke publicly about having children, and it seems that she had no great desire to have them. In 1563, when her councillors pressed her to name a successor following her near-death experience, Elizabeth declared that "the marks they saw on her face were not wrinkles, but pits of smallpox, and that although she might be old God could send her children as He did to Saint Elizabeth, and they (the lords) had better consider well what they were asking, as, if she declared a successor, it would cost much blood to England".[21] Three years later, when Mary, Queen of Scots gave birth to her son and successor, Elizabeth allegedly exclaimed: "The Queen of Scots is the lighter for a boy, and I am but of barren stock!"[22]

In 1580, when she was forty-seven, Elizabeth was very close to marrying the Duke of Anjou, but she knew it was too late for her to produce offspring and informed the French ambassador that if she failed to have children with Anjou, she would agree to have their marriage annulled.[23] In her later years, Elizabeth took offence at her young maids and ladies-in-waiting for marrying behind her back and becoming pregnant, often out of wedlock. She had no sympathy for her pregnant servants, often sending them on errands in an advanced state of pregnancy.

Whether Elizabeth truly was the Virgin Queen she wanted the world to believe, it was inevitable that rumours targeting her chastity would appear. She was, after all, daughter of a queen executed for adultery and a single woman among men. Catherine de Medici, who exercised power in France as regent, told Elizabeth's ambassador that "it is all the hurt that evil men can do to noble women and princes, to spread abroad lies and dishonourable tales of them, and that we of all princes that be women are subject to be slandered wrongfully of them that be our adversaries, other hurt they cannot do to us".[24]

In the 1590s, the French King Henri IV quipped that three questions would never be resolved, one of them being "whether Queen Elizabeth was a maid or no".[25] If her contemporaries never learned the truth, how much more unlikely are we to ever discover the secrets of the Virgin Queen?

NOTES

[1] Henry Clifford, *The Life of Jane Dormer, Duchess of Feria*, p. 87.
[2] Elizabeth Norton, *The Temptation of Elizabeth Tudor: Elizabeth I, Thomas Seymour, and the Making of a Virgin Queen*, p. 120.
[3] An oath taken by midwife Eleanor Pead in 1567 before the Archbishop of Canterbury, quoted in Doreen Evenden, *The Midwives of Seventeenth-Century London*, p. 205.
[4] *Calendar of State Papers, Spain (Simancas),* Volume 1, *1558-1567,* n. 27.
[5] *Calendar of State Papers, Spain (Simancas),* Volume 1, n. 270.
[6] Ibid., 190.
[7] Ibid., Volume 3, n. 343.
[8] Ibid., Volume 1, n. 122.
[9] Mary Anne Everett Green (ed.), *Calendar of State Papers Domestic Series of the Reign of Elizabeth Preserved in Her Majesty's Public Record Office*, p. 534.
[10] *Calendar of State Papers, Spain (Simancas),* Volume 1, n. 251.
[11] Anne Somerset, *Elizabeth I*, p. 43.
[12] *Calendar of State Papers, Spain (Simancas),* Volume 2, n. 408.
[13] *Calendar of State Papers Relating To English Affairs in the Vatican Archives,* Volume 2, n. 458.
[14] Carole Levin, *The Heart and Stomach of a King: Elizabeth I and the Politics of Sex and Power*, p. 80.
[15] Ibid., p. 83.

---

[16] Ibid., p. 84.
[17] Frederick Chamberlin, *The Private Character of Queen Elizabeth*, p. 310.
[18] Ibid., p. 317.
[19] Mary Anne Everett Green (op.cit.)
[20] *Calendar of State Papers, Spain (Simancas)*, Volume 3, n. 253.
[21] Ibid., Volume 1, n. 211.
[22] J.E. Neale , *Queen Elizabeth I*, p. 142.
[23] Estelle Paranque, *Elizabeth I of England through Valois Eyes*, p. 162.
[24] Carole Levin, *The Heart and Stomach of a King: Elizabeth I and the Politics of Sex and Power*, p. 68.
[25] Ibid., p. 66.

Appendix: The Other Tudors, Dawn of the Stuarts & the Change of Childbirth Rituals

Before Henry VIII produced a healthy male heir in 1537, his sisters' children were considered as his possible successors. The King had two sisters: Margaret, born in 1489, and Mary, born in 1496. Margaret married King James IV of Scotland in 1503 and produced several children at great peril to her life. She gave birth to her first child, son James, on 21 February 1507. Margaret, who was seventeen at the time, experienced a difficult labour and remained confined to her private suite for longer than anticipated. James IV made a pilgrimage to St Ninian in March 1507 to pray for Margaret's health, and she later credited her recovery to "the piety and devotion of her husband through St Ninian under God".[1] Unfortunately, Prince James died shortly after his first birthday, on 28 February 1508.

On 15 July 1508, Margaret gave birth to her second child, a girl, "and was in great peril of her life".[2] The baby girl died shortly after a hasty christening ceremony. It remains unknown how far advanced in her pregnancy Margaret was when she gave birth. On 20 October 1509, Margaret gave birth to a healthy baby boy, Arthur, named after her late brother.[3] Unfortunately, the little prince died nine months later, on 14 July 1510.[4] On 10 April 1512, Margaret gave birth to another boy, the future King James V.[5] Margaret became pregnant soon after James's birth and delivered another child, whose sex is unknown, in the winter of 1512.[6] The baby lived long enough to be baptised but died soon after.[7] James IV was killed during the Battle of Flodden on 9 September 1513 when Margaret was in the early stages of her sixth pregnancy. She gave birth to James IV's posthumous son, Alexander, on 30 April 1514.[8]

Margaret enjoyed a brief regency during the minority of her son James V but lost her position when she married Archibald Douglas, Earl of Angus. On 7 October 1515, Margaret gave birth to the only child she would have with Angus: Margaret Douglas, future Countess of Lennox. The baby Margaret, named after her mother, was born when the Dowager Queen of Scots fled Scotland to the safety of her homeland. Margaret later recalled that the fear and jeopardy she was in at the time caused her to be "delivered of a child fourteen days afore my time to my great spoil and extreme danger".[9] She suffered severe pains in her right leg that made it impossible for her to sit up in bed for three weeks following birth. When her servants moved her from the bed, she gave out pitiful "shrieks and cries" and was carried around the castle in a chair.[10]

Mary Tudor, Henry VIII's younger sister, married Louis XII of France in 1514, but the marriage was short-lived and ended three months later with the fifty-two-year-old King's death. Some said that excesses in the royal bedchamber hastened Louis's end. Mary, eighteen at the time of his death, secretly married her brother's friend Charles Brandon, Duke of Suffolk. The couple's first child, a son named Henry, after the King, was born on 11 March 1516.[11] This boy died in his early childhood. More children followed in quick succession: Frances on 16 July 1517, Eleanor c. 1518 and a son Henry, born c. 1523. Mary Tudor Brandon died in 1533 at the age of thirty-seven; the exact cause of her death remains unknown. In one letter to her brother, she wrote about her illness:

"Sire, so it is that I have been very sick, and ill at ease, for the which I was fain to send for Master Peter the physician, for to have holpen me of the disease that I have. Howbeit, I am rather worse than better."[12]

Despite the fact that Mary never accepted Henry VIII's second wife, Anne Boleyn, the King always preferred to be succeeded by her children rather than by Margaret's son James V. Henry's relations with James V were fraught with difficulties due to James's strong pro-French sympathies. Margaret Tudor died intestate on 18 October 1541; the cause of her death was given as palsy.[13] In his 1544 Act of Succession, Henry VIII cut James V out of the line of succession, abhorring the idea of his throne passing to that "beggarly and stupid King of Scots".[14]

Mary Tudor was outlived by three children, but her only son, Henry, Earl of Lincoln, died in 1534 at the age of eleven. Frances and Eleanor lived to adulthood and produced children of their own. Eleanor Brandon married Henry Clifford, Earl of Cumberland, and produced one daughter, Margaret, before dying in 1547. Frances married Henry Grey, Marquis of Dorset, and had three daughters with him: Jane, Katherine and Mary. In 1544, Henry VIII made Frances's children heirs to the throne after his own progeny. When Edward VI died childless in 1553, he cut out Mary and Elizabeth from succession, appointing instead Lady Jane Grey, Mary Tudor's granddaughter, as his direct heiress (like his father, Edward disinherited Margaret Tudor's descendants).

Jane Grey's brief tenure as Queen of England lasted from 6 to 19 July. She was overthrown by Henry VIII's elder daughter, Mary, who became Queen in her own right in 1553 as Mary I. Only sixteen at the time of her brief reign, Jane later asserted that she was poisoned twice: first at the house of the Duke of Northumberland following Edward VI's death and then a second time in the Tower of London, wherein she was awaiting her coronation. She reasoned that she was poisoned in the Tower because "the skin has since that time peeled from my body".[15] Jane Grey was eventually executed in February 1554.

During her first Parliament summoned on 5 October 1553, Mary reinforced her sister's bastardy by proclaiming the legality of the marriage between Henry VIII and Katharine of Aragon. Mary made it clear that she preferred her cousins to succeed her, paying much attention to Margaret Douglas, Countess of Lennox, and Frances Grey, Duchess of Suffolk, daughters of Margaret and Mary Tudor respectively. The other claimant to the throne during Mary's reign was Margaret Clifford, the only surviving daughter of Eleanor Brandon. Queen Mary died without direct heir in 1558 and was succeeded by her younger half sister, Elizabeth.

Queen Elizabeth I famously refused to name a successor for fear of rebellions aiming at dethroning her and placing the next heir on her throne. Unlike her father and brother, Elizabeth believed that the Stuarts, who sprang from Margaret Tudor, had precedence over the descendants of her junior aunt, Mary the French Queen. By the time of Elizabeth's accession in 1558, James V was dead and had been succeeded by his only surviving child, his daughter Mary.

Mary, Queen of Scots was born on 8 December 1542 and crowned as an infant while her mother, Marie of Guise, acted as regent during her minority. When Mary was four years old, her mother sent her to France, where Mary spent her formative years. She married Dauphin Francis and became Queen of France upon his accession in 1558. Francis was a sickly youth and died of an ear infection at the age of sixteen in 1560. Following his death, Mary, Queen of Scots returned to her homeland.

In the early 1560s, Elizabeth I's court was divided into two camps: the Catholics who opted to see Mary, Queen of Scots as Elizabeth's heiress and the Protestants who supported Lady Jane Grey's younger sisters. Katherine and Mary Grey were Elizabeth's closest female kinswomen with a claim to the throne, but Elizabeth hated both of them. Katherine Grey incurred the Queen's wrath when she secretly married Edward Seymour, Earl of Hertford, son of the executed Duke of Somerset. As a claimant to the throne, Katherine's marriage was a matter of state, and Elizabeth placed both lovers in the Tower, separating them for life and annulling their marriage. But the Grey-Seymour union produced two sons: Edward and Thomas, who remained strong claimants to Elizabeth's throne, and this despite the stain of illegitimacy hanging over them. Separated from her husband and children, Katherine Grey became severely depressed and refused to eat. She starved herself to death, dying on 27 January 1568 at the age of twenty-seven.

Mary, Queen of Scots married her kinsman Henry Lord Darnley, son of Margaret Douglas, Countess of Lennox, and thus grandson of Margaret Tudor. In 1566, she gave birth to her only child, the future James VI of Scotland. The twists and turns of Mary, Queen of Scots's fate are well known: she was accused of plotting the death of her husband, Lord Darnley, who was murdered in 1567, married the main suspect, the Earl of Bothwell, and was forced to abdicate in favour of her infant son, James. In

1568, she escaped to England, where she lived out her days as Queen Elizabeth's prisoner, and was executed for plotting Elizabeth's death in 1587.

And yet it was James VI of Scotland, Mary Stuart's only son, who succeeded Elizabeth I in 1603 as James I of England. When James and his wife, Anne of Denmark, arrived to claim the Virgin Queen's crown, they already had three children: Henry, Elizabeth and Charles. In 1605, Queen Anne gave birth to Princess Mary, the first royal baby to be born in England since Jane Seymour gave birth to Edward VI sixty-eight years earlier. Another daughter, Sophia, was born in 1606. Both princesses soon died: Sophia shortly after birth, Mary aged two.

Queen Anne of Denmark's two deliveries were attended by Peter Chamberlen the Elder, who acted as Anne's accoucheur and surgeon. The ritual of withdrawing to the birthing chamber a month before the due date was swiftly abandoned, and with the rise of physicians specialising in childbirth and gynaecology (known as accoucheurs), childbirth was no longer an exclusively female affair. Peter Chamberlen was present when Charles I's wife, Queen Henrietta Maria, gave birth to her first child, a stillborn boy, in 1628. By the time her second son, the future Charles II, was born in 1630, Henrietta Maria had a

French midwife sent by her mother, Marie de Medici, although Chamberlen was also present in the birthing chamber.

Madame Peronne was the apprentice of Louise Bourgeois, who delivered all of Maria de Medici's six children, including Henrietta Maria. Louise was, in her own words, "the first woman of my art to take pen in hand to describe the knowledge God gave to me".[16] She was the first midwife who published books and treatises about women's gynaecological health. The first book on midwifery in English was published in 1671 by midwife Jane Sharp.

By the time James II's Queen, Mary of Modena, gave birth to James Francis Edward Stuart in 1688, male and female members of the royal household were invited to the birthing chamber to witness labour. Princess Anne, James II's younger daughter, related in a letter to her sister Mary:

"The feet curtains of the bed were drawn and the two sides were open. When she was in great pain, the King called in haste for my Lord Chamberlain, who came up to the bedside to show he was there; upon which the rest of the Privy Council did the same thing. Then the Queen desired the King to hide her face with his head and periwig, which he did for she said she could not be brought to bed and have so many men look upon her; for all the Council stood close to the bed feet and the Lord Chancellor upon the step."[17]

And yet despite so many people witnessing the birth of James II's male heir, a story about how a changeling was carried to the Queen's apartments inside a warming pan soon started circulating in England. The fact that the royal couple were Catholic and struggled to produce a healthy child for years added fuel to the whisper campaign questioning James Francis Edward Stuart's legitimacy.

The Stuarts would occupy the English throne for 111 years. Queen Anne, the last Stuart monarch on the throne, died childless in 1714 after experiencing seventeen pregnancies.

NOTES

[1] I'm grateful to Dr Rachel Delman for drawing my attention to this quote from the thesis entitled *The Late Medieval Scottish Queen c. 1371-c. 1513* authored by Amy Victoria Hayes (University of Stirling), p. 131.

[2] John Leslie, *The History of Scotland, from the Death of King James I, in the Year M.CCCC.XXXVI to the Year M.D.LXI*, p. 78.

[3] Ibid., p. 80.

[4] Ibid., p. 81.

[5] Ibid., p. 84.

[6] Ibid., p. 85.

[7] *Letters and Papers, Foreign and Domestic, Henry VIII,* Volume 1, n. 1504.

[8] John Leslie, *The History of Scotland, from the Death of King James I, in the Year M.CCCC.XXXVI to the Year M.D.LXI*, p. 99.

[9] Maria Perry, *Sisters to the King*, p. 180.

[10] *Letters and Papers, Foreign and Domestic, Henry VIII,* Volume 2, n. 1350.

[11] Ibid., n. 1652.

[12] Mary Anne Everett Green, *Lives of the Princesses of England, from the Norman Conquest*, Volume 5, p. 122.

[13] *Letters and Papers, Foreign and Domestic, Henry VIII,* Volume 16, n. 1307.

[14] Ibid., Volume 13 Part 1, n. 56.

[15] *Writings of Edward the Sixth, William Hugh, Queen Catherine Parr, Anne Askew, Lady Jane Grey, Hamilton, and Balnaves*, p. 32.

[16] Louise Burgeois, *Midwife to the Queen of France: Diverse Observations*, trans. Stephanie Ohara, ed. Alison Klairmont Lingo, p. 1.

[17] Sir John Dewhurst, *Royal Confinements*, pp. 23-24.

ACKNOWLEDGMENTS

Writing *Medical Downfall of the Tudors* was an incredible journey. Throughout the process of researching and writing it, I incurred several debts of gratitude.

Like all other books, this one started as an idea in my head. The only difference is that this idea, unlike others, blossomed for years before I could commit myself wholly to embark on this journey. First and foremost I thank Professor Susan Broomhall for the email exchange we had in 2015. Professor Broomhall's article about Elisabeth of Valois's obstetrical history and the conversation about childbearing rituals in sixteenth-century France inspired me to write this book.

Special thanks to the staff at the British Library, National Archives, Victoria and Albert Museum and Kunsthistorisches Museum for their help.

Next, I thank my readers. I love interacting with you on social media; your comments, constructive criticism and suggestions are very valuable to me.

Special thanks to Dr Euan Roger, who so kindly sent me his article about quarantine regulations in Tudor

England. Dr Kate Lister kindly replied to my query about the sixteenth-century "hysterical passion", and Kathryn Warner patiently endured being grilled about rituals surrounding childbirth in medieval/pre-Tudor England.

Twitter turned out to be a great place for posting questions. A special and heartfelt "thank you" goes to the people who helped me out: Ian Coulson, for contacting me about the source discussing Henry VII's death; Dr Helen Newsome, Dr Rachel Delman, Dr Linda Porter and Dr Amy Hayes for their help in finding sources about Margaret Tudor's childbearing history. Special thanks also to Dr Sara Read, Gemma Hollman, Andrea Zuvich and Christine Hartweg. I also thank my online pen pal Magdalena Januszko for helping me with the translations of the Spanish sources.

I would like to give warm and heartfelt thanks to my husband and daughter for their love and support.

Last but not least, I thank my editor, Jennifer Quinlan from *Historical Editorial*, for her professionalism and sharp editing skills.

Selected Bibliography

Primary Sources: Manuscripts

British Library:

"The maner of the remevyng of the Kynges corps frome his oratory or secret closet to his chapalle in his said maner of Richemont." (Arundel MS 26, f. 28.)

Henry VII on his deathbed, (Add MS 45131, f. 54.)

Henry VIII of England: Life, from his falling in love with A. Boleyn to the death of Qu. Katharine of Aragon (MS Sloane 2495.)

Medical recipes devised by King Henry VIII and his royal physicians (MS Sloane 1047.)

Symon Lowe: Letter to W. Andrews, Caesarean operation: Account of, at Mendham (Egerton MS 2713: 1509-1598, f. 16.)

The Pageants of Richard Beauchamp, Earl of Warwick (Cotton MS Julius E IV/3.)

The National Archives:

SP 1/167/14: Undated letter from Katherine Howard to Thomas Culpeper.
SP 1/167/151: Confession of Andrew Maunsay.
SP 1/167/156: Confession of Edward Waldegrave.
SP 1/167/156: Confession of Malyn Tylney.
SP 1/167/159-60: Confession of Jane Boleyn, Lady Rochford.
SP 1/167/161: Confession of Robert Damport.
SP 1/167/162: Confession of Joan Bulmer.

Printed Primary Sources

Bietenholz, P.G. *The Correspondence of Erasmus: Letters 842-992 (1518-1519)*. University of Toronto Press, 1982.

Brantôme, P. *Illustrious Dames of the Court of the Valois Kings.* The Lamb Publishing, 1912.

Brewer, J.S. & Gairdner, J., eds. *Calendar of State Papers, Spain.* Institute of Historical Research (1862-1932).

Brewer, J.S. & Gairdner, J., eds. *Letters and Papers, Foreign and Domestic, of the Reign of Henry VIII.* 28 Volumes. Institute of Historical Research (1862-1932).

Brigden, Susan, ed. *The Letters of Richard Scudamore to Sir Philip Hoby, September 1549-March 1555.* Camden Miscellany, xxx, (Camden Soc. 4th ser. 39, 1990).

Camden, W. *The History of the Most Renowned and Victorious Princess Elizabeth Late Queen of England.* Flesher, 1688.

Carey, R. *Memoirs of Robert Carey.* Alexander Moring Ltd, 1905.

Cavendish, G. *The Life and Death of Cardinal Wolsey.* S.W. Singer, Harding and Leppard, 1827.

Clifford, H. *The Life of Jane Dormer, Duchess of Feria.* Burns & Oates, 1887.

Dowling, M., ed. *William Latymer's Cronickille of Anne Bulleyne.* Camden Miscellany, xxx (Camden Soc. 4th ser. 39, 1990).

Ellis, H. *Original Letters Illustrative of English History*, Volume 2. (2nd series). Harding and Lepard, 1827.

Everett Wood, A. *Letters of Royal and Illustrious Ladies of Great Britain, Three Volumes.* London: H. Colburn, 1846.

Examination of Queen Katherine Howard in Calendar of the Manuscripts of the Marquis of Bath, Preserved at Longleat, Wiltshire. Volume 2. John Falconer, 1907.

Fabyan, R. *The New Chronicles of England and France*. F. C. & J. Rivington, 1811.

Foxe, J. *The Actes and Monuments of the Church*. Hobart Seymour, ed. M. Robert Carter & Brothers, 1855.

Giustiniani, S. *Four Years at the Court of Henry VIII.* Two Volumes. Translated by Rawdon Brown. London: Smith, Elder, 1854.

Gough Nichols, J. *The Chronicle of Queen Jane and of Two Years of Queen Mary.* Camden Society, 1850.

Hall, E. *Hall's Chronicle.* J. Johnson, 1809.

Harris, N. *Privy Purse Expenses of Elizabeth of York*. William Pickerint, 1830.

Harris, N. *Testamenta Vetusta. Two Volumes.* Nicholas & Son, 1826.

Hobby, E., ed. *The Birth of Mankind: Otherwise Named, The Woman's Book*. Routledge, 2017.

Leland, J. *Joannis Lelandi antiquarii de rebus britannicis collectanea.* Richardson, 1770.

Letts, M., ed. *The Travels of Leo of Rozmital*. Hakluyt Society, 2nd ser. 108, 1957.

Loomis, C. "Elizabeth Southwell's Manuscript Account of the Death of Queen Elizabeth [with Text]". *English Literary Renaissance,* Vol. 26, No. 3, Monarchs (1996), pp. 482-509.

Mancini, D. *The Usurpation of Richard III*. Clarendon Press, 1969.

More, C. *The Life of Sir Thomas More*. William Pickering, 1828.

Mueller, J., ed. *Katherine Parr: Complete Works and Correspondence*. University of Chicago Press, 2011.

Nichols, J. *A Collection of All the Wills of the Kings and Queens of England*. Society of Antiquaries, 1780.

Pole, R. *Pole's Defense of the Unity of the Church*. Newman Press, 1965.

Sander, N. *Rise and Growth of the Anglican Schism*. Burns and Oates, 1877.

Sharp Hume, M.A. *Chronicle of King Henry VIII of England*. George Bell and Sons, 1889.

St Clare Byrne, M., ed. *The Lisle Letters*. Six Volumes. The University of Chicago Press, 1981.
Wriothesley, C. *A Chronicle of England During the Reigns of the Tudors, from A.D. 1485 to 1559*. Camden Society, 1875.

Secondary Sources

Arnold, J. *Queen Elizabeth's Wardrobe Unlock'd*. Maney Publishing, 1988.

Bernard, G.W. *Anne Boleyn: Fatal Attractions.* Yale University Press, 2010.

Bernard, G.W. *The King's Reformation*. Yale University Press, 2007.

Borman, T. *Elizabeth's Women: The Hidden Story of the Virgin Queen.* Vintage, 2010.

Borman, T. *The Private Lives of the Tudors: Uncovering the Secrets of Britain's Greatest Dynasty.* Hodder & Stoughton, 2016.

Broomhall, S. *Women's Medical Work in Early Modern France.* Manchester University Press, 2011.

Chamberlin, F. *The Private Character of Queen Elizabeth.* Dodd Mead & Company, 1922.

Childs, J. *Henry VIII's Last Victim: The Life and Times of Henry Howard, Earl of Surrey.* Thomas Dunne Books, 2007.

Denny, J. *Anne Boleyn: A New Life of England's Tragic Queen*. Piatkus Books Ltd, 2005.

Doran, S. *Elizabeth I and Her Circle*. Oxford University Press, 2015.

Eccles, A. *Obstetrics and Gynecology in Tudor and Stuart England.* Croom Helm, 1982.

Erickson, C. *The First Elizabeth*. Macmillan, 2007.

Evans, V.S. *Ladies-in-Waiting: Women Who Served at the Tudor Court.* CreateSpace, 2014.
Evenden, D. *The Midwives of Seventeenth-Century London.* Cambridge University Press, 2000.

Fox, J. *Jane Boleyn: The True Story of the Infamous Lady Rochford.* Ballantine Books, 2009.

Fraser Tytler, P. *England under the Reigns of Edward VI and Mary.* Richard Bentley, 1839.

Friedmann, P. *Anne Boleyn: A Chapter of English History, 1527-1536.* Macmillan and Co., 1884.

Furdel Lane, E. *The Royal Doctors, 1485-1714: Medical Personnel at the Tudor and Stuart Courts.* University of Rochester Press, 2001.

Gladish, D.M. *The Tudor Privy Council.* Redford, 1915.

Gunn, S.J. "The Accession of Henry VIII". *Institute of Historical Research, Volume 64, Issue 155, (October 1991): 278-288.*

Hamilton, D.B. *Shakespeare and the Politics of Protestant England.* University Press of Kentucky, 1992.

Harkrider, F.M. *Women, Reform and Community in Early Modern England.* Boydell Press, 2008.

Harris, J.B. *English Aristocratic Women, 1450-1550: Marriage and Family, Property and Careers.* Oxford University Press, 2002.

Hayward, M. *Dress at the Court of King Henry VIII*. Maney, 2007.

Head, M.D. *The Ebbs and Flows of Fortune: The Life of Thomas Howard, Third Duke of Norfolk*. University of Georgia Press, 1995.

Hibbert, C. *The Virgin Queen: A Personal History of Elizabeth I.* Tauris Parke Paperbacks, 2010.

Holmes, F. *The Sickly Stuarts: The Medical Downfall of a Dynasty.* Sutton Publishing Ltd, 2003.

Hutchinson, R. *The Last Days of Henry VIII: Conspiracy, Treason and Heresy at the Court of the Dying Tyrant.* Phoenix, 2006.

Ives, E. W. *The Life and Death of Anne Boleyn: The Most Happy*. Blackwell Publishing, 2010.

James, S. *Catherine Parr: Henry VIII's Last Love*. The History Press, 2010.

Kelly, H.A. *The Matrimonial Trials of Henry VIII.* Wipf and Stock Publishers, 2004.

Klarwill, V. *Queen Elizabeth and Some Foreigners*. Bentano's, 1928.

Levin, C. *The Heart and Stomach of a King: Elizabeth I and the Politics of Sex and Power*. University of Pennsylvania Press, 2013.

Lipscomb, S. *1536: The Year that Changed Henry VIII*. Lion Hudson, 2009.

Lister, K. *A Curious History of Sex*. Unbound, 2020.

Loach, J. *Edward VI*. Yale University Press, 2014.

Loades, D. *Mary Tudor: A Life*. Basil Blackwell, 1989.

Lockyer, R. *Tudor and Stuart Britain: 1485-1714*. Routledge, 2004.

MacNalty, A. *Henry VIII: A Difficult Patient*. Christopher Johnson, 1952.

Merriman, R.B. *Life and Letters of Thomas Cromwell*. Two Volumes. Clarendon Press, 1902.

Montrose, L. *The Subject of Elizabeth: Authority, Gender, and Representation*. University of Chicago Press, 2006.

Myers, A.R. *The Household of Edward IV*. Manchester University Press, 1959.

North, J. *England's Boy King: The Diary of Edward VI, 1547-1553.* Ravenhall, 2005.
Norton, E. *Anne of Cleves: Henry VIII's Discarded Bride*. Amberley Publishing, 2011.

Norton, E. *Bessie Blount: Mistress to Henry VIII.* Amberley Publishing, 2012.

Norton, E. *Jane Seymour: Henry VIII's True Love.* Amberley Publishing, 2010.

Norton, E. *The Boleyn Women: The Tudor Femmes Fatales Who Changed English History.* Amberley Publishing, 2013.

Paranque, E. *Elizabeth I of England through Valois Eyes: Power, Representation, and Diplomacy in the Reign of the Queen, 1558-1588.* Palgrave Macmillan, 2018.

Parker, G. *Imprudent King: A New Life of Philip II. Yale University Press*, 2015.

Penn, T. *Winter King: The Dawn of Tudor England*. Penguin, 2012.

Pollock, G. *An Epidemiological Odyssey: The Evolution of Communicable Disease Control*. Springer, 2012.

Porter, L. *Katherine the Queen: The Remarkable Life of Katherine Parr*. Macmillan, 2010.

Porter, L. *Mary Tudor: The First Queen.* Piatkus Books, 2009.

Read, S. *Maids, Wives, Widows: Exploring Early Modern Women's Lives, 1540–1740*. Pen & Sword History, 2015.

Read, S. *Menstruation and the Female Body in Early Modern England*. Palgrave Macmillan, 2013.

Riehl, A. *The Face of Queenship: Early Modern Representations of Elizabeth I*. Palgrave Macmillan, 2010.

Russell, G. *Young and Damned and Fair: The Life and Tragedy of Catherine Howard at the Court of Henry VIII*. William Collins, 2017.

Scarisbrick, J.J. *Henry VIII*. University of California Press, 1968.
Schofield, J. *The Rise and Fall of Thomas Cromwell: Henry VIII's Most Faithful Servant*. The History Press, 2011.

Sim, A. *The Tudor Housewife*. The History Press, 2010.

Smith, Lacey B. *Catherine Howard: The Queen Whose Adulteries Made a Fool of Henry VIII*. Amberley Publishing, 2009.

Soberton, S.B. *Golden Age Ladies: Women Who Shaped the Courts of Francis I and Henry VIII*. CreateSpace, 2016.

Starkey, D. *Six Wives: The Queens of Henry VIII*. Vintage, 2004.

Starkey, D. *Elizabeth: The Struggle for the Throne*. Harper Perennial, 2007.

Stone, J.M. *History of Mary I, Queen of England*. Sands & Co., 1901.

Strong, R. *Artists of the Tudor Court*. Victoria & Albert Museum, 1983.

Tallis, N. *Uncrowned Queen: The Fateful Life of Margaret Beaufort, Tudor Matriarch*. Michael O'Mara, 2019.

Tremlett, G. *Catherine of Aragon: Henry's Spanish Queen*. Faber & Faber, 2010.

Varlow, S. "Sir Francis Knollys's Latin Dictionary: New Evidence for Katherine Carey". *Historical Research*, 80 (2007), 315-23.

Walker, G. "Rethinking the Fall of Anne Boleyn". *The Historical Journal*, Vol. 45, No. 1 (Mar., 2002), pp. 1-29.

Warnicke, R.M. *The Rise and Fall of Anne Boleyn: Family Politics at the Court of Henry VIII*. Cambridge University Press, 1991.

Warnicke, R.M. *Wicked Women of Tudor England*. Palgrave MacMillan, 2012.

Weir, A. *Elizabeth of York: A Tudor Queen and Her World*. Ballantine Books, 2013.

Weir, A. *Mary Boleyn: "The Great and Infamous Whore".* Vintage, 2011.

Weir, A. *The Lady in the Tower: The Fall of Anne Boleyn.* Vintage, 2010.

Weir, A. *The Six Wives of Henry VIII.* Vintage, 2007.

Whitelock, A. *Elizabeth's Bedfellows: An Intimate History of the Queen's Court*. Bloomsbury Publishing, 2013.

Whitelock, A. *Mary Tudor: England's First Queen.* Bloomsbury Publishing, 2010.

Wilkinson, J. *Katherine Howard: The Tragic Story of Henry VIII's Fifth Queen.* Hachette UK, 2016.

Williams, P. *Catherine of Aragon: The Tragic Story of Henry VIII's First Unfortunate Wife*. Amberley Publishing, 2013.

Wilson, A. V. *Queen Elizabeth's Maids of Honour and Ladies of the Privy Chamber*. John Lane, 1922.

Wilson, P.K. (ed.) *The Medicalization of Obstetrics: Personnel, Practice and Instruments (Childbirth: Changing Ideas and Practices in Britain and America 1600 to the Present).* Routledge, 1996.

Wroe, A. *Perkin: A Story of Deception*. Vintage, 2004.

Journal Articles

Broomhall, S. "Women's Little Secrets: Defining the Boundaries of Reproductive Knowledge in Sixteenth-century France": Society for the Social History of Medicine Student Essay Competition Winner, 1999, *Social History of Medicine,* Volume 15, Issue 1, April 2002, Pages 1–15.

Hallett, C. "The Attempt to Understand Puerperal Fever in the Eighteenth and Early Nineteenth Centuries: The Influence of Inflammation Theory", *Cambridge Journals Medical History*, 2005 Jan 1; 49(1): 1–28.

Roger, E.C. "To Be Shut Up: New Evidence for the Development of Quarantine Regulations in Early-Tudor England", *Social History of Medicine*, 11 April 2019.

Taviner, M. Thwaites, G. and Gant, V. "The English Sweating Sickness, 1485-1551: A Viral Pulmonary Disease?", *Medical History*, 42 (1999), pp. 96-8.

Made in the USA
Columbia, SC
02 March 2021

33814314R00215